Introductory Circuit Theory

McGRAW-HILL Electrical Engineering Series

Consulting Editor:
Richard G. Meadows
The Polytechnic of North London

Introductory Circuit Theory

J. K. FIDLER

Senior Lecturer
Department of Electrical Engineering Science
University of Essex

McGRAW-HILL Book Company (UK) Limited

London · New York · St Louis · San Francisco · Auckland · Bogotá
Guatemala · Hamburg · Johannesburg · Lisbon · Madrid · Mexico
Montreal · New Delhi · Panama · Paris · San Juan · São Paulo · Singapore
Sydney · Tokyo · Toronto

Published by McGRAW-HILL Book Company (UK) Limited

MAIDENHEAD · BERKSHIRE · ENGLAND

British Library Cataloguing in Publication Data
Fidler, J K
    Introductory circuit theory.
    1. Electric circuits
    I. Title
    621.319′2′01   TK454   79-40654
    ISBN 0-07-084095-4

1 2 3 4 5   SB   8 2 1 0

PRINTED AND BOUND IN GREAT BRITAIN

To Jadwiga

CONTENTS

PREFACE

The subject of circuit theory has enjoyed a prominent position in the teaching of electrical and electronic engineering for many years, and indeed has its origins in the very foundations of electrical science. In recent times, developments in circuit theory have accompanied the technical revolution which has been experienced in the electronics field, and have provided sophisticated tools and techniques which are now being applied in several engineering and other disciplines. This book serves as an introduction to this important and interesting subject.

Circuit theory establishes mathematically the basis of circuit operation, and so enables the engineer to both understand the operation of a circuit through analysis, and to predict the operation of a circuit which he is designing. To be useful, the theory must clearly not involve abstract mathematical concepts which are difficult to assimilate and apparently unrelated to the practical nature of the engineer's work, nor must it require a lengthy mathematical manipulation of such complexity that it destroys his confidence in the results. In short, the justification for the theory must be that it provides a useful and easily applied tool to complement the practical ingenuity of the engineer. With this in mind, this text seeks to introduce the reader to the important fundamental topics in circuit theory. In Chapter 1, the basic components of resistance, capacitance and inductance together with voltage and current sources are considered, and lead to the analysis of simple circuits using Kirchhoff's Laws. It is shown that differential relationships exist between the voltage and current in capacitors and inductors, and Chapter 2 investigates the solution of the differential equations which, as a result, are found to characterize circuit behaviour. For the particular case where the input voltage or current in a circuit varies sinusoidally with time, the direct solution of these differential equations is found to be lengthy and tedious, and the phasor technique is developed in Chapter 3 to deal with this important class of circuit inputs. One important application of phasors is in the analysis of tuned circuits, which find widespread use in electrical and electronic engineering by virtue of their frequency selective properties, and these are studied in Chapter 4.

When analysing the operation of complex circuits, a variety of aids are available. Circuit simplification may be obtained by using the Thévenin and Norton equivalent circuits, and through the use of the star/delta circuit transformation, while nodal and mesh methods of matrix analysis provide a formal but easily applied approach to circuit analysis. These techniques are discussed in Chapter 5.

The first five chapters of the book are restricted to circuits which are linear, that is where linear relationships exist between their output and input signals. Chapter 6 is concerned with nonlinear circuits incorporating diodes and transistors, and it is shown that in many cases, the tools provided by earlier chapters may still be applied, despite the nonlinearity of the devices, by utilizing small signal analysis techniques.

The effectiveness of many circuits (such as amplifiers) is assessed in terms of the power which they can provide to an electrical load. In Chapter 7, methods for extracting the maximum power from a source by power matching are introduced, and the calculation of a.c. power for sinusoidal signals is examined. In particular, it is shown that the phasor technique developed in Chapter 3 provides a very simple means for power calculation.

Finally, Chapter 8 covers the important class of electrical signals which are periodic, that is they have waveforms which regularly repeat in time. The apparent difficulties which would seem to be involved in the analysis of circuits subject to input signals of this type are discounted through the use of Fourier analysis, which resolves a periodic waveform of any complexity into the sum of a series of harmonically related sinusoids. As a result it is found that phasor analysis techniques may then be invoked to determine the circuit response.

This book is aimed at the first year undergraduate level in electrical and electronic engineering degree courses, and should be suitable for students studying similar technological courses. It is assumed that the reader will also be taking introductory courses in circuit design, and in mathematical topics such as differential equations, complex numbers and matrices, although every attempt has been made to fully discuss such topics as they arise.

In conclusion, I must thank Mrs N. Finney and Mrs C. Snape for their proficiency in typing the manuscript of this book, and also many of my friends and colleagues, too numerous to mention, with whom I have had useful discussions over the years. A special word of thanks is due to my wife Jadwiga for her patience and encouragement throughout the project, and to Jennie and Marek for leaving their father to get on with his writing!

JKF

Wivenhoe 1978

1

CIRCUIT COMPONENTS AND CONCEPTS

The operation of all electronic equipment relies at a fundamental level on the movement of electric charge. This charge is carried by electrons, and the movement constitutes a current whose magnitude is determined by the energy supplied to the electrons from some source. At the practical level, electronic components such as the resistor, capacitor, inductor, diode and transistor are used because they exhibit certain useful relationships between the current measured at their terminals and the energy supplied. These components are fundamental in modern electronics, and the terminal relationships when expressed mathematically form the basis of circuit theory. Just as the engineer can assemble components to form a complex electronic circuit, so can he relate his mathematical characterizations of the

1

components to give a characterization of the circuit. While the circuit itself will yield the practical result on the laboratory bench, the mathematical formulation can be used to predict that result. Circuit analysis is therefore the prime motivation for developing a circuit theory.

In this book we shall be considering some important introductory topics in circuit theory. We shall find that these topics provide useful mathematical tools which enable the engineer to understand his circuits, to be able to analyse them, and hence gain insight into their operation. To be useful, these tools must be simple so that they may be easily and quickly applied to give the required result. Indeed, it is often inappropriate to pursue a complex and rigorous mathematical development of a particular circuit problem, simply because the practical spreads in component parameters introduce an uncertainty in circuit operation which renders mathematical precision unnecessary. It is important, therefore, for the reader to appreciate that it is not electronics which supports a sophisticated mathematical circuit theory with the connotations of abstraction and practical irrelevance which the word theory is often taken to imply. Rather, circuit theory is a subject in the service of the electronic engineer, a subject which if ignored reduces the engineer to an over reliance on rules of thumb, but which if appreciated provides the engineer with the opportunity for a complete understanding of his field, and most important the ability to use his increased knowledge to innovate.

In this chapter we shall be considering the basic components and concepts of electronic circuits which provide the foundations for the chapters that follow.

1.1   VOLTAGE, CURRENT, ENERGY AND POWER

As mentioned in the introduction, electronics is concerned with the movement of charge. At the atomic level in materials, this charge is carried by electrons which are extremely light atomic particles which rotate around an atomic nucleus in a series of fixed orbits. The electrons, which have a mass of about 9.1×10^{-31} kg possess a negative charge of magnitude 1.6×10^{-19} coulomb (unit symbol C). To make the atom electrically neutral, the nucleus carries a positive charge which is equal in magnitude to the sum of the electron charges in the surrounding orbits. The electrons are bound in their orbits by the attraction between their negative charges and the positive charge on the nucleus. In some materials, the electrons are all firmly fixed in low energy orbits close to the nucleus, and it is almost impossible for any to break free from the attractive forces. Such materials are known as *insulators*. In *conductors* on the other hand, electrons in the outer atomic orbits suffer only a weak attraction towards the nucleus, and require only a little externally applied energy to break away from the atom, and become free electrons. Copper, aluminium, silver and gold are metals which are used in electronics as conductors. While conductors have many free electrons (for example copper has about $5 \times 10^{28}/\text{m}^3$) and insulators have virtually none, there is another class of materials which fall between these two extremes. For example silicon and germanium, when doped with impurities, have an intermediate number of free electrons, and are hence known as *semiconductors*. Semiconductors find wide application in the construction of transistors and similar solid state components.

If an electric field is applied to a conductor, the free electrons are made to move through the atomic lattice structure of the material. This movement of negative charge constitutes a *current*. The current has a magnitude which is given by the rate at which charge traverses some cross section of the conductor. Current is measured in *amperes* (unit symbol A) where one ampere corresponds to a rate of one coulomb/second. In practice the velocity of electrons required to give quite sizeable currents is extremely low.

Example

In an 0.35 A bicycle lamp the bulb is connected to the battery by copper wires of diameter 1.5 mm. Calculate the velocity of the free electrons in the wire.

Let the velocity of the electrons be u m/s. Then in one second, a volume of $u \times \pi(1.5 \times 10^{-3})^2/4 \text{ m}^3$ will have been swept through the shaded cross-sectional area shown in Fig. 1.1. In copper there are 5×10^{28} electrons in each cubic metre, and each electron carries a charge 1.6×10^{-19} C. The total charge swept through the cross-sectional area is therefore

$$[u \times 5 \times 10^{28} \times 1.6 \times 10^{-19} \times \pi(1.5 \times 10^{-3})^2/4] \text{ C},$$

and this takes place in one second. Therefore,

$$u \times 5 \times 10^{28} \times 1.6 \times 10^{-19} \times \pi \left(\frac{1.5 \times 10^{-3}}{4}\right)^2 = 0.35 \text{ A}$$

giving $u = 2.48 \times 10^{-5}$ m/s. This is an extremely low velocity. Indeed, if the

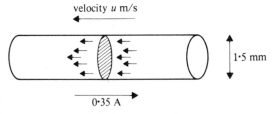

velocity u m/s

1·5 mm

0·35 A

Fig. 1.1 Current flow in a copper wire

connecting wire had a length of one metre, it would take 11.2 hours for the electrons to travel the whole length!

Conventionally, positive current is taken to flow in the opposite direction to the negative charge on the electron. For example, in Fig. 1.1, while the electrons are travelling from right to left, the current of 0.35 A is taken to flow from left to right. The flow of current in a conductor gives rise to a magnetic field which will produce a force on any other conductor also carrying current. In fact, while it has been stated above that a current of one ampere corresponds to the movement of one coulomb of charge in one second across a cross section of conductor, the international definition of the ampere is now taken to be 'that constant current which if maintained in each of two infinitely long straight parallel conductors of negligible cross section, produces a force between them of 2×10^{-7} newton/metre length in vacuo'.

If the charge in a conductor moves with a constant velocity, then this constitutes a constant current. However, if the charge moves in a time varying manner, the current will also vary with time. If the instantaneous current is denoted by i, and charge by q, we then have

$$i = \frac{dq}{dt} \tag{1.1}$$

To make the electrons, and hence the charge, move in a conductor, some energy must be supplied. The electrons acquire potential energy, and in moving from one point to another in a material, a *potential difference* is said to exist between the two points. In electric circuits, this energy, and hence the potential difference, is measured in *volts* (unit symbol V). A potential difference of one volt is said to exist between two points in a circuit if one joule of energy must be expended in moving one coulomb of charge between the points. That is, 1 volt = 1 joule/coulomb. In terms of instantaneous quantities, the potential difference, or voltage v is given by

$$v = \frac{d\epsilon}{dq} \tag{1.2}$$

where ϵ is the instantaneous energy. If charge is continuously moved in a conductor, the energy must be continuously expended. The rate at which energy is expended is known as *power*, and so

$$p = \frac{d\epsilon}{dt} \tag{1.3}$$

where p is the instantaneous power measured in joules/second, or watts (unit symbol W).

Rewriting Eq. (1.3), and using Eq. (1.1) and Eq. (1.2),

$$p = \frac{d\epsilon}{dt} = \frac{d\epsilon}{dq} \cdot \frac{dq}{dt} = vi \tag{1.4}$$

The total energy associated with a potential difference v and the resulting current is therefore

$$\xi = \int p \cdot dt = \int vi \cdot dt \tag{1.5}$$

This energy is often dissipated as heat, although we shall see later that in some electronic components it may actually be stored.

Example

The potential difference across an 0.35 A bicycle lamp is 6 V. Calculate the power dissipated in the lamp, and the energy supplied over a period of one hour.

In the absence of further information, we may take the current and voltage to be constant with time, and so using Eq. (1.4)

$$p = vi = 6 \times 0.35 = 2.1 \text{ W}$$

The total energy is then given by

$$\xi = \int_0^{3600} 2.1 \, dt = 2.1 \times 3600 = 7560 \text{ J}$$

In the case of a lamp, this energy would be dissipated mainly as heat, but also as light.

1.2 RESISTANCE

In practice, the source of energy applied to a circuit may be a battery, signal generator, thermocouple, solar cell, or a variety of other sources. Such sources are said to provide an *electromotive force* (e.m.f.) and they cause some potential difference to be established between the points to which they are applied. As was previously mentioned an electric field is set up in a conductor which, if the potential difference is constant, causes a constant force to be exerted on the electrons, resulting in their movement. According to Newtonian mechanics, the electrons should accelerate, and so acquire an increasing velocity under the influence of this force. However, as the electrons move, they collide with the atoms of the material, and this results in a mean velocity being established which corresponds to a constant current. The magnitude of this current will depend on the atomic structure of the conducting material, and various materials will therefore exhibit a different *resistance* to current flow. In many materials, the current which flows is found to be in proportion to the potential difference, or voltage. In fact it was the German scientist, Ohm, who discovered in the nineteenth century that 'at a constant temperature, the current flowing in a conductor is directly proportional to the applied voltage'. More succinctly, we may write Ohm's Law as

$$v = Ri \qquad (1.6)$$

where R is the *resistance* of the conductor, measured in ohms (unit symbol Ω). Alternatively,

$$i = Gv \qquad (1.7)$$

where $G = 1/R$ is the *conductance*, measured in siemens (unit symbol S). Components which offer a particular resistance are of course common in electronics, and are known as resistors. The symbol for such a component is shown in Fig. 1.2. Particular attention should be paid to the direction which has been assigned to the current and the polarity of the voltage. Remembering that the electrons travel in the opposite direction to conventional current, they will achieve increasing potential as they travel from the terminal marked (−) to the one marked (+). The potential difference, or voltage is therefore measured from the positive to the negative terminal, and this is expressed by annotating a reference arrow in the direction shown. In the rest of this book, the positive and negative signs will be omitted, since the voltage polarity and current direction are evident when the arrow notation is used.

Ohm's Law is an idealised relationship between voltage and current which nevertheless is found to be approximately true for a wide range of components. In some cases, however, components exhibit other characteristics which do not have such a linear relationship between voltage and current. One example is the semiconductor diode, for which $i = I_s(e^{qv/kT} - 1)$, clearly a nonlinear relationship between current and voltage.

Using Eq. (1.6) and Eq. (1.4), alternative expressions for the power dissipated in a resistor may be obtained. Thus,

$$p = vi = i^2R = \frac{v^2}{R} \qquad (1.8)$$

Fig. 1.3 shows two resistors connected in *series*. To maintain continuity

Fig. 1.2 Resistor

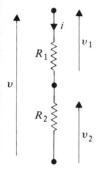

Fig. 1.3 Resistors in series

of charge movement, the same current must flow through both resistors. The voltage v is given by

$$v = (R_1 + R_2)i$$

and the effective resistance is

$$R = \frac{v}{i} = R_1 + R_2$$

To take this further, if n resistors $R_1, R_2 \ldots R_n$ are connected in series, they may be represented by an effective resistance

$$R = \sum_{r=1}^{n} R_r = R_1 + R_2 + \cdots + R_n$$

Returning to Fig. 1.3, it will be seen that

$$v = R_1 i + R_2 i = v_1 + v_2$$

In other words, the voltage developed across both resistors is the sum of the voltages developed across each. Further,

$$\frac{v_2}{v} = \frac{iR_2}{i(R_1 + R_2)} = \frac{R_2}{R_1 + R_2} \tag{1.9}$$

Eq. (1.9) is known as the *potential divider rule* for resistors.

In Fig. 1.4, two resistors are connected in parallel. It is assumed that currents i_1 and i_2 flow as shown. Both resistors have a common potential difference, and so

$$i_1 = \frac{v}{R_1}, \quad i_2 = \frac{v}{R_2}$$

Again, continuity considerations in this case suggest $i = i_1 + i_2$, that is

$$i = v \left(\frac{1}{R_1} + \frac{1}{R_2} \right)$$

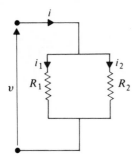

Fig. 1.4 Resistors in parallel

The effective resistance is therefore given by

$$\frac{1}{R} = \frac{i}{v} = \frac{1}{R_1} + \frac{1}{R_2} \qquad (1.10)$$

or

$$R = \frac{1}{1/R_1 + 1/R_2} = \frac{R_1 R_2}{R_1 + R_2} \qquad (1.11)$$

As an abbreviated notation, Eq. (1.11) is sometimes written as $R = R_1 \| R_2$. Eq. (1.10) states that the effective conductance is found by adding the conductances of the parallel components, and this leads to the obvious extension in the general case, that is

$$\frac{1}{R} = \sum_{r=1}^{n} \frac{1}{R_r}$$

Finally, it will be noted that

$$\frac{i_2}{i} = \frac{v/R_2}{v\left(\dfrac{1}{R_1} + \dfrac{1}{R_2}\right)} = \frac{R_1}{R_1 + R_2} \qquad (1.12)$$

Eq. (1.12) is known as the *current divider rule* for resistors.

Example

Calculate the effective resistance of the circuit shown in Fig. 1.5.

In this circuit, the resistors have values in kilohms, or thousands of ohms. The 3 kΩ and 6 kΩ resistors in parallel have an effective resistance of $(3 \times 6)/(3 + 6) = 2$ kΩ, which becomes $7 + 2 = 9$ kΩ when the 7 kΩ resistor is added. Turning to the parallel 18 kΩ resistor, this gives a final effective resistance of $(9 \times 18)/(9 + 18) = 6$ kΩ.

In addition to kilo-, several other prefixes are used in electronics to indicate multiplication by power of ten. Those commonly used are summarised in Table 1.1.

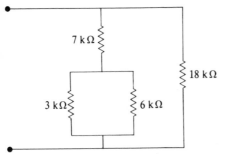

Fig. 1.5 Resistor circuit

Table 1.1

Prefix	Symbol	Factor
mega-	M	10^6
kilo-	k	10^3
milli-	m	10^{-3}
micro-	μ	10^{-6}
nano-	n	10^{-9}
pico-	p	10^{-12}

The potential divider rule and current divider rule introduced above are very useful means of determining voltages and currents in a circuit without recourse to Ohm's Law, as the following example shows.

Example

Find the voltage v and the current i in the circuit shown in Fig. 1.6.
 The voltage v appears across the effective resistance $(3 \times 6)/(3 + 6) =$

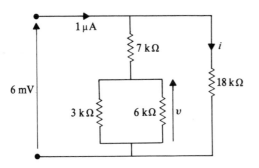

Fig. 1.6 Resistor circuit

$2\,k\Omega$. Using the potential divider rule (Eq. (1.9)),

$$v = 6\,\text{mV} \times \frac{2\,k\Omega}{(2+7)\,k\Omega} = \frac{4}{3}\,\text{mV}$$

The current i flows through the $18\,k\Omega$ resistor which is in parallel with an effective resistance of $2+7=9\,k\Omega$. Using the current divider rule (Eq. (1.12))

$$i = 1\,\mu\text{A} \times \frac{9\,k\Omega}{(9+18)\,k\Omega} = \frac{1}{3}\,\mu\text{A}$$

Finally, the reader will note that the voltage across the $18\,k\Omega$ resistor is given by Ohm's Law as $18\,k\Omega \times (\frac{1}{3})\,\mu\text{A} = 6\,\text{mV}$ as expected.

In practice, resistors are manufactured using a variety of techniques and materials. Examples are wire-wound, metal film, and carbon composition, and these types can be made to produce resistors having values ranging from fractions of one ohm through to tens of megohms.

1.3   CAPACITANCE

The symbol for a capacitor is shown in Fig. 1.7(a), together with the conventions for voltage polarity and current direction. As the symbol suggests, a capacitor is a component which consists of a pair of metal plates which are physically separated. In some practical capacitors, the plates simply have air between them; in others, a *dielectric* such as polyester, ceramic or mica is interposed between the plates to increase the capacitive effect which will now be discussed. In electrolytic capacitors, electrochemical reaction is induced between the plates to give a gaseous dielectric only a few molecules thick. Air spacing is usually used when a variable capacitor is required, while for fixed capacitors, the plates are usually made from metal foil or film, which is assembled to form a compact component.

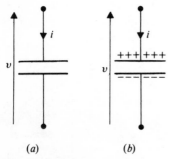

(a)   (b)

Fig. 1.7 Capacitor

If a potential difference is established between the terminals of a capacitor, then initially a current will flow. Negatively charged electrons will move in the opposite direction to conventional current, and since they cannot traverse the space between the plates, a negative charge will accumulate on the lower plate as shown in Fig. 1.7(b). Those electrons leaving the upper plate will leave a positive charge whose magnitude will be equal to that on the lower plate. This process will continue until the force of attraction between the opposite charges on the two plates of the capacitor is equal and opposite to the force experienced by the electrons due to the applied potential difference; at this point the current will fall to zero. The capacitor is then said to be *charged*. If the source of energy which established the applied potential difference is now removed, the charge would remain *stored* on the capacitor plates, and indeed could only be redistributed to the original state if the capacitor were connected across some circuit (such as a resistance) which would permit the electrons to move, and establish a continuous current. This current would dissipate power in the resistance, and so we see that the capacitor in its charged state stores energy. Electronic flash units in photography and capacitor discharge ignition systems rely on this property in their operation.

The relationship between the charge stored on one plate of the capacitor and the applied voltage is given by

$$q = Cv \qquad (1.13)$$

where C is the *capacitance* measured in *farads* (unit symbol F). Like Ohm's Law, Eq. (1.13) defines a linear relationship between charge and voltage. If the voltage varies with time, then from Eq. (1.13),

$$\frac{dq}{dt} = C\frac{dv}{dt}$$

or

$$i = C\frac{dv}{dt} \qquad (1.14)$$

The current which flows into the terminals of a capacitor is therefore proportional to the time derivative of the applied voltage. Alternatively, Eq. (1.14) may be written (assuming $i = 0$ for $t < 0$) as:

$$v = \frac{1}{C}\int_0^t i\,dt + v(0) \qquad (1.15)$$

where $v(0)$ is the initial voltage on the capacitor at time $t = 0$. Note that no current can actually flow between the plates of a capacitor. Eq. (1.14) and Eq. (1.15) simply indicate that the movement of charge within the component constitutes a current when measured at the capacitor terminals. If a constant voltage is applied to the terminals of a capacitor, then apart from the instant of application (which corresponds to $dv/dt = \infty$), Eq. (1.14) shows that no current will subsequently flow, since the capacitor will then be charged. However, it will be seen that if the applied voltage varies linearly with time, then a constant current will flow. This is the principle often used in oscilloscope timebases and waveform generators to produce sawtooth and triangular waveforms.

Example

The voltage across a $1\,\mu\text{F}$ capacitor is found to vary in time according to the sawtooth waveform shown in Fig. 1.8. Determine the waveform of the current.

Over the first 1.5 ms, the voltage increases linearly with slope $3/(1.5 \times 10^{-3}) = 2 \times 10^3$ V/s. Thus, using Eq. (1.14), $i = 10^{-6} \times 2 \times 10^3 = 2$ mA. After this time, the voltage decreases linearly, with slope $-3/(0.5 \times 10^{-3}) = -6 \times 10^3$ V/s for 0.5 ms. In this case $i = -10^{-6} \times 6 \times 10^3 = -6$ mA. After this the process repeats itself, and so the current waveform is as shown in Fig. 1.9.

To find the energy stored in a capacitor after a time T seconds during which a time variable voltage v has been applied, we may use Eq. (1.5), i.e.,

$$\xi = \int_0^T vi \, dt = \int_0^T v \cdot C \frac{dv}{dt} \cdot dt$$

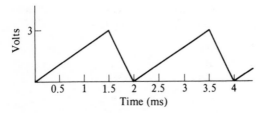

Fig. 1.8 Voltage waveform on a capacitor

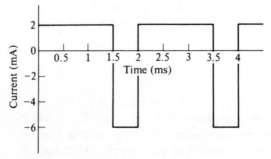

Fig. 1.9 Waveform of capacitor current

Assuming that $v = 0$ at time $t = 0$, and changing the variable of integration, this may be written as

$$\xi = C \int_0^{v,(t=T)} v \cdot dv = \frac{1}{2} Cv^-$$ (1.16)

The energy stored in a capacitor at any time is therefore proportional to the square of the voltage across the capacitor *at that time*. It is independent of the manner in which the voltage previously varied.

We may now turn to consider the effective capacitance produced by the series and parallel combination of capacitors. Fig. 1.10 shows two capacitors connected in series.

Using Eq. (1.15),

$$v_1 = \frac{1}{C_1} \int i \cdot dt, \quad v_2 = \frac{1}{C_2} \int i \cdot dt$$

and

$$v = v_1 + v_2$$

$$\therefore \quad v = \left(\frac{1}{C_1} + \frac{1}{C_2}\right) \int i \cdot dt = \frac{1}{C} \int i \cdot dt$$

giving an effective capacitance

$$C = \frac{C_1 C_2}{C_1 + C_2}.$$

(For n capacitors connected in series, the effective capacitance is thus given by $1/C = \Sigma_{r=1}^n 1/C_r$)

Also

$$\frac{v_2}{v} = \frac{1/C_2}{1/C_1 + 1/C_2} = \frac{C_1}{C_1 + C_2}$$ (1.17)

which is the potential divider rule for capacitors.

Fig. 1.11 shows two capacitors in parallel. In this case we have

$$i = i_1 + i_2 = C_1 \frac{dv}{dt} + C_2 \frac{dv}{dt}$$

$$= (C_1 + C_2) \frac{dv}{dt}$$

Thus the effective capacitance is $C = C_1 + C_2$, and in the general case of

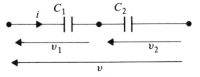

Fig. 1.10 Capacitors in series

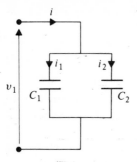

Fig. 1.11 Capacitors in parallel

n capacitors connected in parallel,

$$C = \sum_{r=1}^{n} C_r$$

The current divider rule for capacitors is given by

$$\frac{i_2}{i} = \frac{C_2}{C_1 + C_2}$$

The unit of capacitance, the farad, is extremely large for practical purposes, and values ranging from a few pF to a few thousand μF are generally encountered in practice. On the few occasions when higher values are required, they may be obtained by connecting together several lower value capacitors in parallel to give the desired capacitance.

Example

Two capacitors, of value $1\,\mu$F and $0.5\,\mu$F are connected in series, and charged up to 10 V. Determine the charge on each capacitor, and the energy stored.

The arrangement is shown in Fig. 1.12. Using the potential divider rule

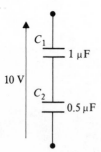

Fig. 1.12 Example of two capacitors in series

for capacitors (Eq. 1.17), the voltage v_1 on capacitor C_1 is given by

$$v_1 = 10 \cdot \frac{0.5 \,\mu\text{F}}{(1+0.5)\,\mu\text{F}} = \frac{10}{3} \text{ V}$$

$$\therefore \quad q_1 = 10^{-6} \times \frac{10}{3} = \frac{10}{3} \,\mu\text{C}$$

and

$$\xi_1 = \frac{1}{2} C_1 v_1^2 = \frac{10^{-6}}{2} \times \left(\frac{10}{3}\right)^2 = 5.56 \,\mu\text{J}$$

For the capacitor C_2

$$v_2 = 10 \cdot \frac{1 \,\mu\text{F}}{(1+0.5)\,\mu\text{F}} = \frac{20}{3} \text{ V}$$

$$\therefore \quad q_2 = 0.5 \times 10^{-6} \times \frac{20}{3} = \frac{10}{3} \,\mu\text{C}$$

and

$$\xi_2 = \frac{0.5 \times 10^{-6}}{2} \times \left(\frac{20}{3}\right)^2 = 11.11 \,\mu\text{J}$$

The total energy stored is $(5.56 + 11.11) = 16.67 \,\mu\text{J}$. This may be checked by calculating that the effective capacitance of the series combination which is $(1 \times 0.5)/(1 + 0.5) = \frac{1}{3} \,\mu\text{F}$. The applied voltage is 10, and so the energy is $(\frac{1}{2}) \times (\frac{1}{3}) \times (10)^2 = 16.67 \,\mu\text{J}$ as expected.

Finally, it will be noted that the same charge is stored on each capacitor. This is because the same charging current flowed through both capacitors for the same time, and therefore accumulated the same charge on each.

1.4 INDUCTANCE

If a current flows through a conductor, it causes a magnetic flux to be set up in the medium surrounding the conductor. By winding the conductor into a coil, the magnetic field may be strengthened, and is measured in terms of the *flux linkages* ϕ associated with the current i flowing in the coil. The flux linkages are simply given by the product of the flux due to one turn of the coil multiplied by the total number of turns. In an ideal medium such as air, it is found that the flux linkage is directly proportional to the current flowing, that is

$$\phi = Li \tag{1.18}$$

Here, L is the *inductance* of the coil or inductor, and is measured in *henries* (unit symbol H). If the current in the coil is changing with time, it will give rise to a changing flux which in cutting the turns of the coil will induce an e.m.f. within it. This is Faraday's Law, and the voltage induced within the coil is given by

$$v = -\frac{d\phi}{dt} = -L\frac{di}{dt} \qquad (1.19)$$

The negative sign in Eq. (1.19) indicates that the induced voltage in the coil opposes the potential difference which causes the changing current i. This is embodied in Lenz's Law, which states that the current flows in such a direction (in the coil) as to oppose (through Faraday's Law) the effect which produced it (the applied potential difference). Thus, in terms of the applied potential difference, we may write

$$v = L\frac{di}{dt} \qquad (1.20)$$

or alternatively (assuming $v = 0$ for $t < 0$)

$$i = \frac{1}{L}\int_0^t v \cdot dt + i(0) \qquad (1.21)$$

where $i(0)$ is the initial current through the inductor at time $t = 0$.

Eq. (1.20) and Eq. (1.21) are the terminal relationships for the inductor, and the symbol for this component is shown in Fig. 1.13.

In practice, inductors are often would in coils around magnetic materials such as iron and ferrites which increase the inductance over that obtained in air. In such cases, however, the range of currents over which Eq. (1.18) then applies is found to be limited owing to the nonlinear effect of saturation and hysteresis. Practical values for inductors range from several henries down to a few μH.

Example

A potential difference of 4 mV is established across the terminals of a 10 μH inductor. Calculate the current which flows.

Fig. 1.13 Inductor

Using Eq. (1.21), we have

$$i = \frac{1}{10 \times 10^{-6}} \int_0^t 4 \times 10^{-3} \, dt + i(0) = (400t + i(0))A$$

The current i is seen to increase linearly with time, and unless the applied voltage is changed, it would increase without limit. This technique for producing a *ramp* (that is, a linear variation) of current is used in television receivers to deflect the electron beam and hence the illuminated spot in the cathode ray tube.

Fig. 1.14 shows two inductors in series. Providing the magnetic fluxes from each inductor do not interact, then the effective inductance L is found from

$$v = v_1 + v_2 = L_1 \frac{di}{dt} + L_2 \frac{di}{dt} = L \frac{di}{dt}$$

i.e.,

$$L = L_1 + L_2$$

Thus, the inductances add to give the effective inductance. This result obviously extends to the general case of n inductors in series, when

$$L = \sum_{r=1}^{n} L_r$$

Two inductors are connected in parallel in Fig. 1.15. In this case, (assuming again no interaction of magnetic flux),

$$i = i_1 + i_2 = \frac{1}{L_1} \int v \, dt + \frac{1}{L_2} \int v \, dt = \frac{1}{L} \int v \, dt$$

i.e.,

$$\frac{1}{L} = \frac{1}{L_1} + \frac{1}{L_2} \quad \text{or} \quad L = \frac{L_1 L_2}{L_1 + L_2}$$

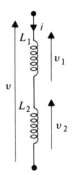

Fig. 1.14 Inductors in series

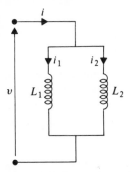

Fig. 1.15 Inductors in parallel

Again, in the general case,

$$\frac{1}{L} = \sum_{r=1}^{n} \frac{1}{L_r}$$

The rules for the series and parallel connection of inductors are seen to be the same as those which were found for resistors, and the reader may care to confirm that similar potential divider and current divider rules apply.

If a current is flowing in an inductor as the result of an applied potential difference, and that current is then reduced to zero, Lenz's Law and Faraday's Law suggest that an e.m.f. will be induced in the inductor to oppose this change of current. In some practical circumstances, where the current is reduced to zero by opening a switch, the induced voltage has sufficient magnitude to cause a spark across the switch contacts. There must therefore be some energy stored in the inductor, which (if the conductor from which it is constructed can be assumed resistanceless, and if the magnetic field it produces does not react with any external objects) must be equal to the energy supplied to the inductor. Following the approach used for the capacitor, if the applied voltage $v = 0$ at time $t = 0$, then after a time T,

$$\xi = \int_0^t vi \cdot dt = \int_0^t i L \frac{di}{dt} \cdot dt = L \int_0^{i(t=T)} i \cdot di = \frac{1}{2} L i^2 \qquad (1.22)$$

The energy stored in an inductor at any time is therefore proportional to the square of the current flowing through the inductor at that time.

When finding the effective inductance of inductors connected in series and parallel, it was stressed that there was assumed to be no interaction of their magnetic fields. We shall now consider the case where this is not true. Figure 1.16 shows two inductors which are arranged such that their magnetic fields interact, that is, the coils are *coupled*. This may be accomplished, for example, by winding the coils on the same former with the

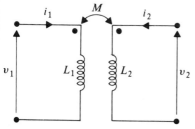

Fig. 1.16 Coupled inductors

turns in close proximity to each other. Now a current i_1 flowing in L_1 will produce a magnetic flux, some of which will link with L_2. If this flux is changing, it will induce, (according to Faraday's Law) an e.m.f. in L_2 in a direction depending on the relative orientation of the turns of L_2 compared with L_1. Equally, an e.m.f. will be induced in L_1 due to a changing current i_2. This may be expressed mathematically as

$$\left. \begin{aligned} v_1 &= L_1 \frac{di_1}{dt} \pm M_{12} \frac{di_2}{dt} \\ v_2 &= \pm M_{21} \frac{di_1}{dt} + L_2 \frac{di_2}{dt} \end{aligned} \right\} \tag{1.23}$$

It may be shown that $M_{12} = M_{21} = M$, the *mutual inductance* between the two inductors.

The dot notation is often used to indicate the polarity of the voltage induced by mutual coupling which may be positive or negative as shown in Eqs. (1.23). In Fig. 1.16, if the current i_1 flowing into the dotted end of L_1 is increasing positively, then the convention defines the induced voltage in L_2 to be positive at the dotted end of L_2 with respect to its other end, and the positive sign applies in Eqs. (1.23).

The energy stored in a pair of coupled coils shown in Fig. 1.16 may be found from

$$\begin{aligned} \xi &= \int v_1 i_1 \cdot dt + \int v_2 i_2 \cdot dt \\ &= \int \left[L_1 i_1 \frac{di_1}{dt} + M i_1 \frac{di_2}{dt} + M i_2 \frac{di_1}{dt} + L_2 i_2 \frac{di_2}{dt} \right] \cdot dt \\ &= \frac{1}{2} L_1 i_1^2 + M \int \left(i_1 \frac{di_2}{dt} + i_2 \frac{di_1}{dt} \right) \cdot dt + \frac{1}{2} L_2 i_2^2 \\ &= \frac{1}{2} L_1 i_1^2 + M i_1 i_2 + \frac{1}{2} L_2 i_2^2 \end{aligned} \tag{1.24}$$

The minimum value of the mutual inductance M is clearly zero, since in that case the coils become uncoupled, and Eqs. (1.23) and Eq. (1.24) reduce to those obtained previously. To find the maximum value of M, let one of the currents in Fig. 1.16 be reversed by changing the polarity of one of the coils. Then from Eq. (1.24)

$$\xi = \frac{1}{2} L_1 i_1^2 - M i_1 i_2 + \frac{1}{2} L_2 i_2^2 \tag{1.25}$$

Eq. (1.25) may now be used to find the minimum energy which may be stored in this situation. First, we find the value of say i_1 which minimises the energy from

$$\frac{d\xi}{di_1} = L_1 i_1 - M i_2 = 0, \quad \text{i.e.,} \quad i_1 = \frac{M}{L_1} i_2$$

Substituting in Eq. (1.25), this gives

$$\xi_{\min} = \frac{1}{2} L_1 \left(\frac{M i_2}{L_1}\right)^2 - M \left(\frac{M}{L_1} i_2\right) i_2 + \frac{1}{2} L_2 i_2^2$$

$$= \frac{1}{2} i_2^2 \left(L_2 - \frac{M^2}{L_1}\right) \tag{1.26}$$

Now $\xi_{\min}$ cannot be negative, since the coils are only capable of storing energy—they cannot generate it. Eq. (1.26) therefore gives

$$L_2 \geqslant \frac{M^2}{L_1} \text{ or } M \leqslant \sqrt{L_1 L_2}$$

Sometimes this is written as $M = k\sqrt{L_1 L_2}$, where k is known as the *coefficient of coupling*, and $k \leqslant 1$.

Using Eq. (1.23), the effects of mutual coupling when coils are connected in series or parallel may now be found. For example, Fig. 1.17(a) shows two coupled coils connected in series. Noting the dot convention and Eqs. (1.23), we have

$$v_1 = (L_1 + M) \frac{di}{dt}, \quad v_2 = (M + L_2) \frac{di}{dt}$$

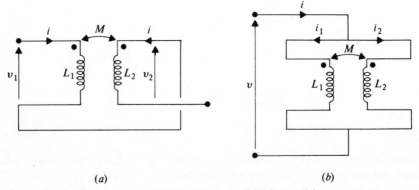

(a)   (b)

Fig. 1.17 Coupled inductors connected (a) in series (b) in parallel

and $v = v_1 + v_2$ is the total voltage across both coils. Therefore,

$$v = (L_1 + 2M + L_2)\frac{di}{dt}$$

from which we see that the effective inductance is $L = (L_1 + 2M + L_2)$.

The coupled inductors are connected in parallel in Fig. 1.17(b), and they have a common voltage v. Eqs. (1.23) in this case are

$$v = L_1 \frac{di_1}{dt} + M \frac{di_2}{dt}$$

$$v = M \frac{di_1}{dt} + L_2 \frac{di_2}{dt}$$

Solving these equations for the currents, it is found that

$$\frac{di_1}{dt} = v \left[\frac{L_2 - M}{L_1 L_2 - M^2}\right]; \quad \frac{di_2}{dt} = v \left[\frac{L_1 - M}{L_1 L_2 - M^2}\right]$$

The effective inductance is given by

$$v = L \frac{di}{dt} = L \frac{di_1}{dt} + L \frac{di_2}{dt} = Lv \left[\frac{L_1 + L_2 - 2M}{L_1 L_2 - M^2}\right]$$

and so

$$L = \frac{L_1 L_2 - M^2}{L_1 + L_2 - 2M}$$

In some applications, great care is taken to ensure that no coupling takes place between inductors. At radio frequencies (rf), for example, the inductors are placed in screening cans to minimize the interaction of the magnetic fields. In many cases, however, the coupling is intentional, and the configuration of coupled coils is known as a *transformer*. Transformers find application from power distribution to radio and audio circuits, and make use of the ability to induce a voltage in one circuit by means of a current flowing in a coupled circuit.

1.5 VOLTAGE AND CURRENT SOURCES

In the previous sections of this chapter, it has been assumed that some energy source has been available to establish the potential difference across the terminals of a component, and hence produce a certain current flow. The battery, signal generator, thermocouple and solar cell have already been cited as examples of such sources. The term *voltage source* is used to describe a source of energy (or e.m.f.) which establishes a potential difference across its terminals. If that potential difference is unaffected by the current flow, then the source is said to be *ideal*. Figure 1.18 shows the

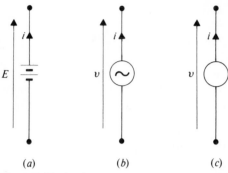

Fig. 1.18 Ideal voltage sources

symbols often used for ideal voltage sources. Figure 1.18(a) shows the symbol for a battery, or d.c. voltage source. The abbreviation d.c. (direct current) is used rather confusingly to indicate that the terminal voltage of the battery is constant with time. Note the current direction associated with the source. Since the battery is a *source* of energy, and causes current to flow, the relative directions of voltage and current are the reverse of those of the resistor, capacitor and inductor which act as energy *sinks*. Figure 1.18(b) shows an a.c. (alternating current) source. In this case the voltage is usually taken to be a sinusoidal function of time, and more will be said about this later. Fig. 1.18(c) is the general symbol used for a voltage source where the voltage may be d.c., a.c., or any other function of time.

Example

Find the currents flowing in the resistor and capacitor in Fig. 1.19.

Since the sources are ideal, they will maintain their terminal voltages independent of the current which flows. The voltage across the capacitor is therefore v, and the current which will flow in the capacitor is given by

$$i_C = C \frac{dv}{dt} = 10^{-6} \times 400 \times 3 \cos (400\,t) = 1.2 \cos (400\,t) \text{ mA}$$

Now the potential difference across the resistor is $6 - 3 \sin (400\,t)$ volts,

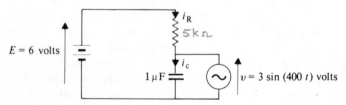

Fig. 1.19 Circuit example

and so the resistor current will be

$$i_R = \frac{6 - 3 \sin (400 \, t)}{5 \times 10^3} = 1.2 - 0.6 \sin (400 \, t) \text{ mA}$$

The a.c. voltage in the example above was expressed in the form $v = V_p \sin (\omega t)$. Here V_p is the *peak* value or *amplitude* of the sinusoidal voltage. This is seen from Fig. 1.20 which shows v plotted against ωt. As the time t proceeds, the sinusoid repeats itself, each cycle starting after a *period* T seconds given by $\omega T = 2\pi$. The reciprocal $f = 1/T$ is known as the *frequency* of the sinusoid, and is measured in cycles/second, or *hertz* (unit symbol Hz). Thus, $\omega = 2\pi f$, and this quantity is known as the *angular frequency*. Since ωt is expressed in radians, ω is measured in radians/second (rad/s).

An alternative way of measuring or defining a sinusoidal quantity is by its mean or average value. Clearly the mean value taken over one period will be zero. Over half a period however,

$$V_{av} = \frac{1}{T/2} \int_0^{T/2} V_p \sin (\omega t) \, dt = \frac{2 \, V_p}{T} \left[-\frac{1}{\omega} \cos (\omega t) \right]_0^{T/2}$$

Recalling that $\omega T = 2\pi$, this becomes

$$V_{av} = \frac{2 \, V_p}{2\pi} [-\cos (\pi) + \cos (0)] = \frac{2 \, V_p}{\pi} = 0.637 \, V_p \qquad (1.27)$$

This average value is an important measure because some measuring instruments (for example the moving coil meter) indicate the average value of the quantity they are measuring. With a sinusoidal voltage, such an instrument would read zero, the average value. However, if the voltage is *full wave rectified* to produce the waveform shown in Fig. 1.21, then the instrument would read $0.637 \, V_p$.

A further measure of a sinusoidal voltage is obtained by considering the average power which such a voltage source would dissipate in a resistor.

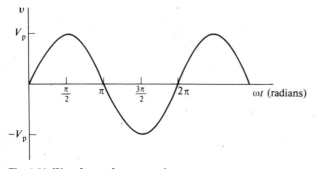

Fig. 1.20 Waveform of an a.c. voltage

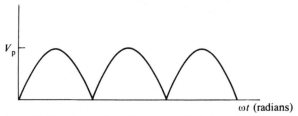

Fig. 1.21 Waveform of a full wave rectified sinusoid

The instantaneous power is given by

$$p = \frac{v^2}{R} = \frac{V_p^2}{R} \sin^2{(\omega t)}$$

The average power taken over one period is then

$$P = \frac{1}{T} \int_0^T \frac{V_p^2}{R} \sin^2{(\omega t)}\, \mathrm{d}t$$

$$= \frac{V_p^2}{2RT} \int_0^T [1 - \cos{(2\,\omega t)}]\, \mathrm{d}t$$

$$= \frac{V_p^2}{2RT} \left[t - \frac{1}{2\omega} \sin{(2\,\omega t)} \right]_0^T = \frac{V_p^2}{2R}$$

Now consider a d.c. source of voltage E_{rms} applied to another resistor R. The continuous (and hence average) power dissipated in this resistor will be $\dfrac{(E_{rms})^2}{R}$. The average powers dissipated in each resistor will therefore be the same when

$$\frac{E_{rms}^2}{R} = \frac{V_p^2}{2R}, \text{ i.e., } E_{rms} = \frac{V_p}{\sqrt{2}} = 0.707\, V_p \qquad (1.28)$$

E_{rms} is known as the *root-mean-square* (or r.m.s.) value of the sinusoid. It is the equivalent d.c. voltage which would cause the same average power to be dissipated in a resistor as the a.c. voltage. The r.m.s. value of a source is not restricted to sinusoids of course, and in the case of a general voltage v it is given, according to the development above, as

$$E_{rms} = \frac{1}{T} \left[\int_0^T v^2\, \mathrm{d}t \right]^{1/2}$$

where T is the period over which the measurement is taken. The domestic mains supply is usually given in terms of its r.m.s. value. For example, if this is 240 volts r.m.s., then the mains supply has a *peak* value of $240 \times \sqrt{2} = 339.4$ volts, and a *peak to peak* value of $339.4 - (-339.4) \approx 679$ volts.

Many a.c. measuring instruments which respond to the mean value of a

nusoid are recalibrated to indicate r.m.s. value. The factor by which the
istrument must be recalibrated may be found from Eq. (1.27) and Eq.
1.28). From the former, $V_p = (\pi V_{av})/2$, and so in the latter, $E_{rms} = \pi V_{av}/(2\sqrt{2}) = 1.11 V_{av}$. The required factor $(E_{rms}/V_{av}) = 1.11$ is known as
ie *form factor* of the sinusoid.

In practice, no voltage source can be ideal, since otherwise an arbitrarily
irge power could be extracted from it by connecting a resistance across its
:rminals, and reducing the resistance towards zero. Even the best prac-
ical sources are limited in the power which they can supply. From the
efinition of an ideal voltage source, it will be understood that a practical
·r non-ideal voltage source will not maintain its terminal voltage in-
lependently of the current flowing. In fact the terminal voltage generally
lecreases as the current increases, so limiting the maximum power sup-
·lied. This effect is often seen in a motorcar if the starter motor is engaged
vhile the headlights are switched on. The large currents taken from the
·attery by the starter motor cause the battery terminal voltage to reduce,
.nd the headlights dim.

A simple way to model a non-ideal voltage source is by means of an ideal
·ource connected in series with a resistance known as the *internal* or
·utput resistance of the nonideal source. This is shown in Fig. 1.22(a).

The output or terminal voltage v_0 is given by $v_0 = v - ir$, and a plot of v_0
.gainst i is shown in Fig. 1.22(b). This form of characteristic is usually an
.cceptable approximation to the true characteristics of a practical voltage
·ource.

In just the same way that it is possible to define an ideal voltage source
vhich maintains a terminal voltage independent of the current flowing (or
n other words, independent of the circuit components in the *load*) it is also
·ossible to define a *current source* which maintains a terminal current
ndependent of the load. The general symbol for a current source is shown
n Fig. 1.23. A potential difference will exist between the terminals of the
iource, and will be fixed by the load into which the current is flowing.
Unlike voltage sources, no special symbols are in general use to differen-

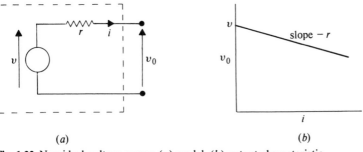

(a)   (b)

Fig. 1.22 Non ideal voltage source (a) model, (b) output characteristic

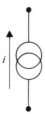

Fig. 1.23 Current source

tiate between d.c., a.c. and general current sources. As in the case of th
a.c. voltage source, a sinusoidal current source $i = I_p \sin(\omega t)$ may be define
in terms of its peak value I_p, its half period average value $0.637\, I_p$, or its r.m.
value $0.707\, I_p$.

Example

Determine the unknown voltage and current in Fig. 1.24.

The battery is connected directly across the $2\,k\Omega$ resistor, and s
impresses a potential difference of $10\,V$ across it. Therefore, i
$\frac{10}{(2 \times 10^3)} = 5\,mA$. The current of $3\,mA$ from the current source wi
develop a potential difference across the $5\,k\Omega$ resistor of $3 \times 10^{-3} \times 5 \times 10^3$
$15\,V$. The voltage established across the current source is therefore v
$15 + 10 = 25\,V$.

The concept of a current source is sometimes difficult to grasp, probab
because unlike voltage sources such as batteries, current sources are n
available over the shop counter to the layman. However, current source
are used to a large extent in modern electronics, being realised by fair
simple transistor circuits. In practice they are non-ideal, and so they cann
supply a current which is independent of the load to which they ar
connected. This may be modelled as shown in Fig. 1.25(a), where again, r
known as the source or output resistance. In this case the non-ide
behaviour arises because not all the current i issuing from the ideal sourc
will flow into a load connected to it—some flows into r according to th
current splitting rule. As the load resistance increases, a greater proportio
of i flows in r, thus increasing the terminal voltage v of the current sourc

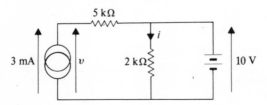

Fig. 1.24 Circuit example

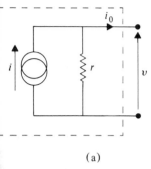   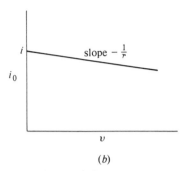

(a)   (b)

Fig. 1.25 Non ideal current source (a) model, (b) output characteristic

The output current is therefore given by $i_0 = i - \left(\dfrac{v}{r}\right)$, and this is plotted in Fig. 1.25(b).

The sources which have been described so far have been *independent* sources. This means that their terminal characteristics are fixed—a voltage source has a defined terminal voltage and a current source a defined terminal current. Frequently, however, *dependent* sources are used in electronics. The hi-fi amplifier is a good example of a dependent voltage source, since it provides an output voltage which is dependent on the input voltage to the amplifier. In this case the output voltage will be a magnified version of the input voltage, although amplification is not a necessary characteristic of a dependent source. The triangle symbol shown in Fig. 1.26(a) is often used for a dependent source, providing it is known what type of source it represents.

The symbols shown in Fig. 1.26(b)–(e) show the alternative representation for the four basic types of dependent source. Fig. 1.26(a) shows a voltage controlled voltage source (VCVS), sometimes called a *voltage amplifier*, although the *gain* of the amplifier $K = \dfrac{v_2}{v_1}$ does not necessarily exceed unity. The VCVS senses an input voltage and produces an output voltage which is related to it by the gain K. In the same way, the *current controlled current source* (CCCS) or *current amplifier* in Fig. 1.26(c) has a current source at its output which is dependent on the current flowing in its input. Figure 1.26(d) represents a *voltage controlled current source* (VCCS), or *transconductance* amplifier, since the output current is related to the input voltage by the constant g_m which has the dimension of conductance. g_m is often known as the *mutual conductance* of the amplifier. The configuration in Fig. 1.26(e) on the other hand is a *transresistance* amplifier since it is a *current controlled voltage source* (CCVS) which gives its constant r_m the dimensions of resistance.

It will be noted that no current can flow into the inputs of the voltage

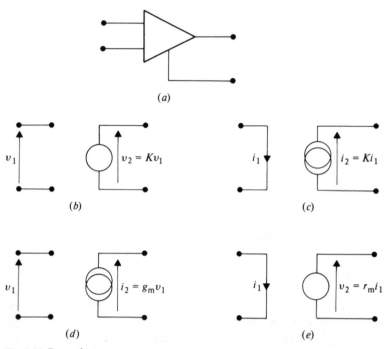

Fig. 1.26 Dependent sources

controlled sources of Fig. 1.26(b) and (d). The inputs of these sources are said to be *open circuits*. Conversely, the current controlled sources of Fig. 1.26(c) and (e) have inputs which are *short circuits*, that is no voltage will be developed between the input terminals when an input current flows. In practice non-ideal controlled sources will meet neither of these ideals, but will have a finite input resistance which is made as high as possible for voltage controlled sources, and as low as possible for current controlled sources. In this way, the dependent source will not disturb a circuit into which its input is connected.

Example

The ideal voltage amplifier shown in Fig. 1.27 has unity gain. If the capacitor is initially uncharged, determine the amplifier output voltage as a function of time.

In this circuit, only one input terminal is shown to the amplifier. This convention is used when the other input is grounded. Since the amplifier is ideal, its input will be an open circuit, and so all the current i will flow into the capacitor. Thus,

$$i = 10^{-4} \frac{dv_C}{dt}$$

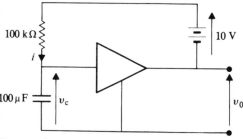

Fig. 1.27 Bootstrap ramp generator

The current i may be found by considering the potential difference across the resistor. At its lower end, the voltage is v_C, whilst at the upper end, the voltage is $(10 + v_0)$. The potential difference is therefore $(10 + v_0 - v_C)$ volts. However, the amplifier has unity gain, and so $v_0 = v_C$, and the resistor voltage is therefore 10. This gives a current

$$i = \frac{10}{10^5} = 10^{-4} \frac{\mathrm{d}v_0}{\mathrm{d}t}$$

and so

$$\frac{\mathrm{d}v_0}{\mathrm{d}t} = 1$$

Since the capacitor is initially uncharged, $v_0 = t$ volts, that is the output voltage increases linearly with time at the rate of 1 V/s. The amplifier, battery and resistor in this example effectively constitute a current source of magnitude $\left(\frac{10}{10^5}\right)$ A = $100\,\mu$A. This has been accomplished by maintaining the voltage across the resistor constant, a technique known as *bootstrapping*.

Voltage sources, whether dependent or independent, may be connected in series to give an equivalent source whose magnitude is the algebraic sum of the constituent source voltages. Ideal voltage sources must not be connected in parallel, however, since unless each source had precisely the same e.m.f., then it would be impossible for each source to maintain its terminal voltage independent of the load. Similarly, current sources may be connected in parallel and the constituent currents summed algebraically to give the equivalent source current.

The series connection of ideal current sources is not allowed as this would not meet the requirement for continuity of current in the conductors connecting the sources.

1.6 KIRCHHOFF'S LAWS

In the previous sections of this chapter, the idea of continuity of current has been used to help determine the effects of connecting components in series or parallel. In addition, the potential differences across components in series have been added to determine the potential difference across the composite series connection. We may now formalize these ideas by introducing *Kirchhoff's Laws*. Kirchhoff's Current Law (KCL) is concerned with current flow at a point in a circuit, and states that 'at any point in a circuit, the algebraic sum of currents is zero'. This is illustrated in Fig. 1.28. At the junction or *node* denoted N, Kirchhoff's Current Law gives $i_1 - i_2 - i_3 + i_4 = 0$. Alternatively, this may be written as $i_1 + i_4 = i_2 + i_3$ which expresses the fact that the total current leaving the node is equal to the total current arriving at the node, providing the necessary continuity of current flow.

Example

Derive an expression for the voltage v in the circuit shown in Fig. 1.29. Applying KCL to the upper junction of components, we find

$$i = i_C + i_L + i_R$$

i.e.,

$$i = C\frac{dv}{dt} + \frac{1}{L}\int v \, dt + \frac{v}{R}$$

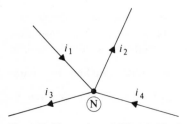

Fig. 1.28 Illustration of Kirchhoff's Current Law

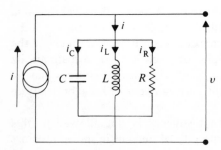

Fig. 1.29 Circuit example

This is an *integrodifferential* equation in v. Differentiating with respect to t,

$$C\frac{d^2v}{dt^2} + \frac{1}{R}\frac{dv}{dt} + \frac{v}{L} = \frac{di}{dt}$$

This expression is now a linear differential equation with constant coefficients. The solution of such equations is considered in Chapter 2.

Kirchhoff's Voltage Law (KVL) states that 'around any closed path in a circuit, the algebraic sum of voltages is zero'. Thus, with reference to Fig. 1.30, if the path shown is traversed in the clockwise direction, $v_1 - v_2 - v_3 - v_4 + v_5 = 0$. It will be seen that Kirchhoff's Voltage Law is really a statement of the conservation of energy since the total work done or energy expended in taking charge around a closed path must be zero.

Example

Determine the voltage v_3 in the circuit shown in Fig. 1.31.
    KVL gives $v_1 - v_2 - v_3 = 0$

i.e., $$v_1 = v_2 + v_3 = L\frac{di}{dt} + v_3$$

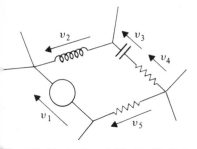

Fig. 1.30 Illustration of Kirchhoff's Voltage Law

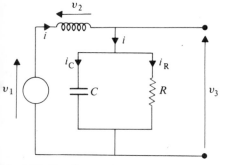

Fig. 1.31 Circuit example

Applying KCL to the upper junction of the capacitor and resistor

$$i = i_C + i_R = C \frac{dv_3}{dt} + \frac{v_3}{R}$$

Thus

$$v_1 = L \frac{d}{dt} \left(C \frac{dv_3}{dt} + \frac{v_3}{R} \right) + v_3$$

or

$$LC \frac{d^2v_3}{dt^2} + \frac{L}{R} \frac{dv_3}{dt} + v_3 = v_1$$

Again, we find that the expression is a linear differential equation with constant coefficients.

1.7 LINEARITY

When a circuit is constructed by connecting together components of the type which have been discussed in this chapter, it will be with some purpose in mind. In electrical terms, circuits are usually designed so that one or more voltage or current sources connected as *inputs* to the circuit cause some specified voltages or currents to be developed as *outputs* of the circuit. For example in a public address system, the microphone provides the input voltage to the amplifier, whose output voltage is used to drive the loudspeaker, this being an amplified version of the input voltage. To avoid the need to refer to voltage *or* current when describing inputs and outputs, the general descriptive term *signal* is often used.

The components considered earlier all have one important property—they are *linear*. This is because characteristics such as $v = Ri$, $i = C(dv/dt)$ and $v = L\left(\frac{di}{dt}\right)$ represent linear relationships between the voltage v and current i, which means that if one of these quantities (v or i) is multiplied by a constant, then the other will be multiplied by the same constant. By virtue of Kirchhoff's laws, which show that a current (or voltage) may be determined by the linear combination of other currents (or voltages), this property of linearity is extended to cover all circuits which are constructed using linear components. The potential divider rule (Eq. (1.9)) and current divider rule (Eq. (1.12)) are examples of the expression of this linearity, albeit for simple circuits. In the general case, we can say that if an input signal x is applied to a linear circuit and gives rise to an output signal y, then an input kx will give rise to an output ky. This is known as the *principle of proportionality*, or sometimes as the *principle of homogeneity*. The important practical implication of this principle is that if an output of a circuit is calculated for a particular value of input, then the circuit does not have to be reanalysed if the input is, say, doubled—one simply doubles the output previously obtained.

The principle of proportionality does not just cover the case where there is only one circuit input. Consider the circuit shown in Fig. 1.32 which has two inputs, v_1 and v_2. The current i_1 will be taken to be the output. To find i_1, first note that using KCL, the current through R_3 will be $i_1 + i_2$. KVL applied to the closed paths v_1, R_1, R_3 and v_2, R_2, R_3 then gives

$$v_1 = i_1 R_1 + (i_1 + i_2)R_3 = i_1(R_1 + R_3) + i_2 R_3 \tag{1.29}$$

$$v_2 = i_2 R_2 + (i_1 + i_2)R_3 = i_1 R_3 + i_2(R_2 + R_3) \tag{1.30}$$

Eq. (1.30) gives

$$i_2 = \frac{v_2 - i_1 R_3}{(R_2 + R_3)}$$

Substituting in Eq. (1.29)

$$v_1 = i_1(R_1 + R_3) + \frac{R_3(v_2 - i_1 R_3)}{(R_2 + R_3)}$$

$$= i_1\left[\frac{(R_1 + R_3)(R_2 + R_3) - R_3^2}{(R_2 + R_3)}\right] + \frac{v_2 R_3}{R_2 + R_3}$$

Finally, solving for i_1,

$$i_1 = v_1 \cdot \frac{(R_2 + R_3)}{R_1 R_2 + R_1 R_3 + R_2 R_3} - v_2 \cdot \frac{R_3}{R_1 R_2 + R_1 R_3 + R_2 R_3} \tag{1.31}$$

In Eq. (1.31) it is seen that if the inputs v_1 and v_2 are both multiplied by k, the output i_1 will also be multiplied by k, so satisfying the principle of proportionality. Eq. (1.31) suggests a more convenient way to calculate i_1. If v_2 were set to zero in Fig. 1.32, the current i_1 due to v_1 alone could be found. According to Eq. (1.31), this must be

$$i_{1(v_2=0)} = v_1 \cdot \frac{(R_2 + R_3)}{R_1 R_2 + R_1 R_3 + R_2 R_3}$$

Similarly, with v_1 set to zero, the current i_1 due to v_2 alone may be found,

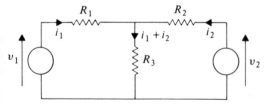

Fig. 1.32 Example of the principle of superposition

and this must be

$$i_{1(v_1=0)} = -v_2 \cdot \frac{R_3}{R_1R_2 + R_1R_3 + R_2R_3}$$

Adding these two results gives the current i_1 when both input sources are present. This approach is, in fact, the application of the *principle of superposition* which is obeyed by all linear circuits. In general terms, the principle states that in a linear circuit if an input x_1 alone gives rise to an output y_1, while an input x_2 gives rise to an output y_2, then if x_1 and x_2 are both input, the output will be $y_1 + y_2$. The inputs x_1 and x_2 may be applied at the same or different parts of the circuit, and the principle may be extended to any number of inputs.

In order to be able to apply the principle of superposition, it is important to understand the effect on a circuit of setting an input source to zero. Fig. 1.33(a) shows two voltage sources connected in series together with a resistor. Applying KVL, or simply noting that the potential difference across R is $v_a - v_b$, it is seen that $i = \frac{(v_a - v_b)}{R}$. If now v_b is set to zero, then $i = \frac{v_a}{R}$. This is precisely the current which would flow in the circuit of Fig. 1.33(b), in which the voltage source v_b has been replaced by a short circuit. Hence, *if a source voltage is reduced to zero, the source may be replaced by a short circuit.*

The circuit shown in Fig. 1.34(a) enables a similar result to be derived for a current source. Using KCL, the current in the resistor is $i_a + i_b$, and so the

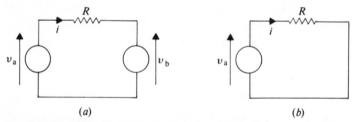

(a)   (b)

Fig. 1.33 The effect of setting a voltage source to zero

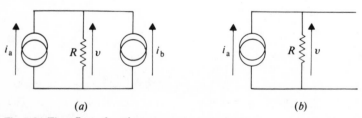

(a)   (b)

Fig. 1.34 The effect of setting a current source to zero

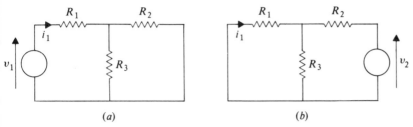

Fig. 1.35 Application of the principle of superposition to Fig. 1.32

voltage developed across the resistor is $v = (i_a + i_b)R$. If now i_b is reduced to zero, $v = i_a R$, and this is the voltage developed across R in Fig. 1.34(b). Here, the current source has been removed, leaving an open circuit. In this case we see that *if a current source is reduced to zero, it may be replaced by an open circuit.*

Returning now to the circuit of Fig. 1.32, i_1 may be found by setting $v_2 = 0$, to give the circuit of Fig. 1.35(a). By virtue of the short circuit replacing the source v_2, R_2 and R_3 are in parallel, and so the current i_1 is given by

$$i_1 = \frac{v_1}{R_1 + R_2 \| R_3} = \frac{v_1}{R_1 + \dfrac{R_2 R_3}{(R_2 + R_3)}} = \frac{v_1(R_2 + R_3)}{R_1 R_2 + R_1 R_3 + R_2 R_3} \qquad (1.32)$$

In Fig. 1.35(b), the source v_1 has been replaced by a short circuit. In this case R_1 and R_3 are in parallel. Using the potential divider rule, the voltage across this parallel combination will be

$$v_2 \cdot \frac{R_1 \| R_3}{R_2 + R_1 \| R_3} = v_2 \cdot \frac{R_1 R_3}{R_1 R_2 + R_1 R_3 + R_2 R_3}$$

and so

$$i_1 = -v_2 \cdot \frac{R_3}{R_1 R_2 + R_1 R_3 + R_2 R_3} \qquad (1.33)$$

The negative sign in Eq. (1.33) takes account of the fact that with the polarity of voltage source shown, positive current would flow through R_1 in a direction opposite to that shown for i_1. Adding Eq. (1.32) and Eq. (1.33) according to the principle of superposition, Eq. (1.31) is obtained as expected.

Example

Find the voltage v in the circuit shown in Fig. 1.36.

Replacing the current source by an open circuit, as in Fig. 1.37(a), the potential divider rule gives $v = 9 \times 6\,k\Omega/(12\,k\Omega + 6\,k\Omega) = 3\,V$. In Fig. 1.37(b), the voltage source has been replaced by a short circuit. As a result,

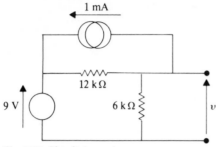

Fig. 1.36 Circuit example

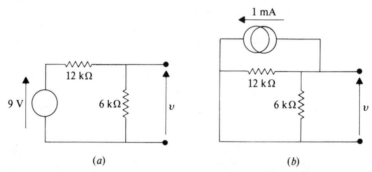

(*a*) (*b*)

Fig. 1.37 Application of the principle of superposition to Fig. 1.36

the two resistors are in parallel, with an effective resistance of $\dfrac{(12 \times 6)}{(12 + 6)}$ = 4 kΩ. The current of 1 mA flows through this parallel combination in the direction shown, and so $v = -1\,\text{mA} \times 4\,\text{k}\Omega = -4\,\text{V}$. Adding the two results, $v = 3 - 4 = -1\,\text{V}$. Thus, the output voltage v has a magnitude of 1 V, but with a polarity which is in fact the reverse of that shown in Fig. 1.36.

Example

The voltage amplifier in Fig. 1.38 has a gain m. Determine the output voltage v_0 in terms of the input v_{in}.

In this example there are two sources, the input source and the con-

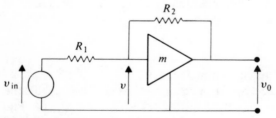

Fig. 1.38 Circuit example

trolled voltage source at the output of the amplifier. Using the principle of superposition, the input voltage to the amplifier v_1 is given by

$$v = v_{in} \cdot \frac{R_2}{R_1 + R_2} + v_o \cdot \frac{R_1}{R_1 + R_2} \tag{1.34}$$

Now the amplifier has a gain m, and so $v_o = mv$. Using this in Eq. (1.34),

$$v_o = mv_{in} \cdot \frac{R_2}{R_1 + R_2} + mv_o \cdot \frac{R_1}{R_1 + R_2}$$

Solving for v_o,

$$v_o = v_{in} \cdot \frac{mR_2}{R_1 + R_2 - mR_1}$$

The principles of proportionality and superposition are clearly important tools for the analysis of linear circuits. Indeed, if a circuit obeys these two principles then it is by definition linear, since they represent the necessary and sufficient conditions for linearity.

1.8 SUMMARY

This chapter has been concerned with the basic concepts and components of electronic circuits. We have seen that in circuit analysis, it is the relationship between the flow of charge, or current, and the supplied energy per unit charge, or voltage, which is of interest. When considering components, this relationship is either algebraic ($v = Ri$), differential ($i = C\left(\dfrac{dv}{dt}\right)$, $v = L\left(\dfrac{di}{dt}\right)$) or integral ($v = \dfrac{1}{C}\int i \, dt$, $i = \dfrac{1}{L}\int v \, dt$). Kirchhoff's voltage and current laws indicate that a voltage or current in a circuit can be expressed as a linear combination of other voltages or currents. These laws together with the linear circuit component characteristics give rise to linear relationships between input and output signals which obey the principles of proportionality and superposition. In particular, superposition provides a very powerful tool for circuit analysis.

As has been seen in examples in this chapter, circuits which include capacitive, inductive and resistive components have input/output relationships which are linear differential equations. Much of circuit theory is concerned with the solution of such equations, and this topic is dealt with in the next chapter.

CHAPTER 1

Problems

1. A copper strip, 1 cm wide and 2 mm thick, carries a current of 2 A. Calculate the mean velocity of the free electrons in the strip. (Answer: 1.25×10^{-5} m/s)
2. When two resistors are connected in series, they provide an effective resistance of 8.3 kΩ. When connected in parallel, the resistance is 1.8 kΩ. Determine the values of the resistors. (Answer: 2.7 kΩ, 5.6 kΩ)
3. Find the effective resistance of the circuit shown in Fig. 1.39. (Answer: 4.36 kΩ)
4. When a resistor of value R Ω is connected as shown in Fig. 1.40(a), the effective resistance of the circuit is also R Ω. Determine R. Hence, find the resistance of the infinite ladder of 1 Ω resistors shown in Fig. 1.40(b). (Answer: 1.62 Ω, 2.73 Ω)
5. Calculate the effective capacitances C_1 and C_2 which would be measured between each set of terminals in the bridged T circuit shown in Fig. 1.41. If a potential difference of 1 V is established across the left hand pair of terminals, find the value of C such that this capacitor stores 0.09 J of energy.

$$\left(\text{Answer: } C_1 = \frac{9C + 6}{6C + 8}, \ C_2 = \frac{9C + 6}{6C + 5}, \ C = 0.89 \text{ F or 2 F}\right)$$

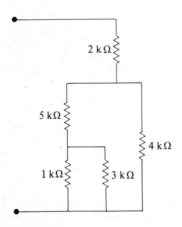

Fig. 1.39 Resistive circuit for problem 3

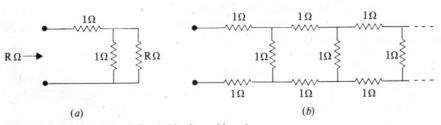

(a)

(b)

Fig. 1.40 Analysis of a resistive ladder in problem 4

6. When a battery of e.m.f. E volts is switched onto the simple RC circuit shown in Fig. 1.42, the capacitor voltage varies with time according to $v = E(1 - e^{-t/RC})$, where t is the time in seconds after the switch is thrown. Show that, as $t \to \infty$, the total energy supplied by the battery to the resistor is the same as that supplied to the capacitor.

7. An uncharged 1 μF capacitor is supplied with a current which halves every 1 ms, as shown in Fig. 1.43. Find the ultimate voltage on the capacitor. (Answer: 2 V)

8. A capacitor of value 1 μF is charged to 10 V. It is then connected in parallel with an uncharged capacitor of the same value. Determine the total energy stored (i) before, (ii) after the connection is made.
(Answer: (i) 0.05 μJ, (ii) 0.025 μJ)   (i) 0.05 mJ (ii)

9. A voltage ramp $v = 3 \times 10^{-3}t$ (where t is the time in seconds) is applied to an inductor of value 2 mH at $t = 0$ secs. Calculate the current in the inductor after 1 second. (Answer: 0.75 A)

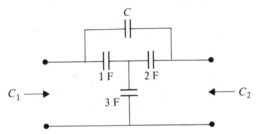

Fig. 1.41 Bridged-T capacitor circuit (problem 5)

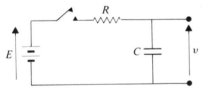

Fig. 1.42 Simple RC charging circuit (problem 6)

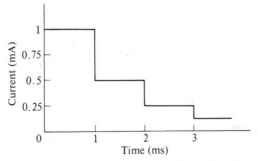

Fig. 1.43 Current source waveform for problem 7

10. A 10 mH inductor is connected in series with a capacitor of value 1 μF. A sinusoidal current $i = \sin 10^4 t$ flows in the circuit. Find (i) the voltage across the capacitor, (ii) the voltage across the inductor, (iii) the voltage across the series connection of the two components.
(Answer: (i) $-100 \cos 10^4 t$, (ii) $100 \cos 10^4 t$, (iii) 0)

11. Two inductors, of value 4 H and 1 H, are coupled, having a coefficient of coupling $k = 0.5$. What are the maximum and minimum values of inductance which may be obtained by connecting these inductors in series or parallel?
(Answer: 7 H, 0.75 H)

12. Find the currents i_1 and i_2 in Fig. 1.44.
(Answer: 1 mA, 0.5 mA)

13. A non-ideal voltage source has the characteristic shown in Fig. 1.45. Find the output voltage when a 300 Ω resistor is connected to the terminals of the source.
(Answer: 1.5 V)

14. A non-ideal current source is modelled by an ideal source of value 100 mA in parallel with a 200 Ω resistor. Find the current which would flow in a 50 Ω resistor connected to the source.
(Answer: 80 mA)

15. Calculate the average and r.m.s. values of the sawtooth waveform shown in Fig. 1.46.
(Answer: 1 V, 1.414 V)

16. A rectangular pulse train of amplitude E volts has mark:space ratio $m:1$. Derive (a) the r.m.s. value, (b) the mean value of the signal. For what

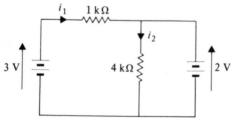

Fig. 1.44 D.C. resistor circuit for problem 12

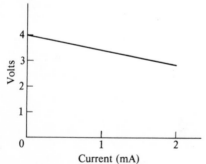

Fig. 1.45 Non ideal source characteristic (problem 13)

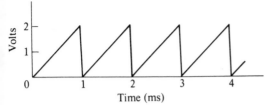

Fig. 1.46 Sawtooth voltage waveform (problem 15)

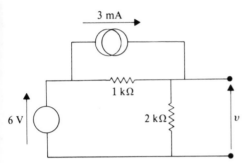

Fig. 1.47 Circuit for problem 17

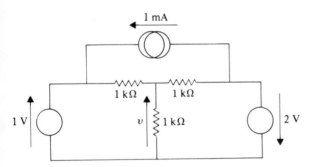

Fig. 1.48 Circuit for problem 18

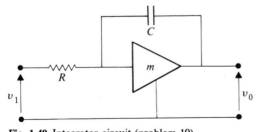

Fig. 1.49 Integrator circuit (problem 19)

mark:space ratio does the signal have the same r.m.s. value as a sinusoid of peak value E volts?

$$\left(\text{Answer: } E\left[\frac{m}{m+1}\right]^{1/2}; \frac{mE}{m+1}; 1:1\right)$$

17. Using the principle of superposition, calculate the voltage v and current i, in the circuit shown in Fig. 1.47.
(Answer: 6 V, 3 mA)

18. Determine the voltage v in the circuit of Fig. 1.48.
(Answer: $-\frac{1}{3}$ V)

19. The circuit of Fig. 1.49 incorporates a voltage amplifier (VCVS) of gain m. Show that as $m \to -\infty$ the output voltage becomes

$$v_o = -\frac{1}{CR}\int v_1 \, dt.$$

TIME DOMAIN ANALYSIS—
TRANSIENT RESPONSE

In Chapter 1 it was seen that the terminal characteristics of capacitors and inductors are governed by differential relationships, and that when these components are connected into circuits with resistors and energy sources, the circuits are described mathematically by linear differential equations with constant coefficients. The formulation and solution of these equations is known as *time domain analysis*, which is a technique of circuit analysis which finds the *transient response* of a circuit, that is its response as a function of time.

Circuit analysis is of fundamental importance in electronics because it allows the engineer to predict the operation of circuits. It is experience gained from analysis which enables the engineer to design or synthesise circuits which will operate in some specified way, and this of course is the ultimate objective of electronic engineering.

In this chapter we shall establish the general rules for time domain analysis by investigating some specific circuit examples.

2.1   RESISTOR–CAPACITOR (RC) CIRCUITS

In the circuit shown in Fig. 2.1, a battery of e.m.f. E volts is to be applied via a switch to a resistor and an uncharged capacitor connected in series. The switch will be closed at an arbitrarily chosen time origin $t = 0$ s. The voltage applied to the circuit is said to be a *step function* since it steps from 0 to E volts at time $t = 0$. This circuit will be analysed to find the subsequent capacitor voltage v_C. Assuming a current i will flow after the switch is closed, then for the resistor, Ohm's Law gives

$$i = \frac{E - v_C}{R} \qquad (2.1)$$

and for the capacitor

$$i = C \frac{dv_C}{dt} \qquad (2.2)$$

Eliminating i between these equations,

$$C \frac{dv_C}{dt} = \frac{E - v_C}{R}$$

or

$$RC \frac{dv_C}{dt} + v_C = E \qquad (2.3)$$

Eq. (2.3) is a linear first order differential equation whose solution will give the capacitor voltage v_C as a function of E, R, C and time t. Before proceeding to this solution, it is instructive to consider intuitively what will happen in the circuit after the switch is closed. Since the capacitor is uncharged prior to the switch being closed (and so the voltage on its plates will be zero), one of two things might happen at the instant of closure—

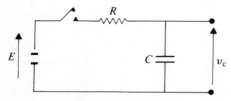

Fig. 2.1 Simple RC charging circuit

either the capacitor voltage will remain momentarily at zero, or will instantaneously jump up to some finite value v_{C0}. If such a jump does occur, then the energy stored in the capacitor will change instantaneously from zero to $\frac{1}{2}Cv_{C0}^2$. Recalling that power is the rate of supply of energy, an infinite power flow will be required to establish the change in energy. Also, since $\frac{dv_C}{dt}$ would be infinite, Eq. (2.2) shows that an infinite current will flow in the circuit. Clearly, neither of these events could occur in a practical circuit, and so we conclude that *it is impossible to change the voltage on a capacitor instantaneously.* (The charge q on a capacitor is given by $q = Cv$, and so a similar statement can be made for charge). Thus at the instant of switch-on, the capacitor voltage will be zero. However a current i will flow in the capacitor according to Eq. (2.2), the current relating to the rate of change of capacitor voltage with time. At the instant of switch on, therefore, the capacitor is passing a current but has no voltage across its plates. In other words, *at time $t = 0$ s, the capacitor behaves as a short circuit.* After $t = 0$ s, the capacitor voltage will rise from zero at a rate determined by the value of i in Eq. (2.2). But as v_C rises, the current i will drop according to Eq. (2.1), and so the rate at which v_C rises and the capacitor charges, will decrease with time. When v_C reaches E volts, no current will flow in the resistor, and thus the capacitor voltage will increase no further, and will stay at $v_C = E$ volts. In this condition, the capacitor has a voltage across it, but no current passes through its terminals. Therefore, *with a constant voltage across its terminals, the capacitor behaves as an open circuit.*

It is worthwhile committing the three statements in italics above to memory, because although they have been made by considering the behaviour of a capacitor in a particular circuit, they are generally true, and provide a useful means for establishing initial and final conditions in circuits.

With the qualitative assessment of the manner in which the capacitor charges up to the battery voltage, we may now return to Eq. (2.3) to consider the quantitative aspects of the solution. To solve the equation

$$RC \frac{dv_C}{dt} + v_C = E \qquad (2.3)$$

a variety of methods are available. However, we shall adopt the *method of undetermined coefficients*. In this approach a form of solution to Eq. (2.3) is suggested, and then the unknown coefficients in the suggested solution are determined. In fact, the solution of n-th order linear differential equations, of which Eq. (2.3) is an example, can be split into two parts. If Eq. (2.3) is written as

$$RC \frac{dv_C}{dt} + v_C = E + 0 \qquad (2.4)$$

this expresses the apparently strange fact that the input to the circuit is the sum of E volts and zero volts! The reason for this will be given shortly. Now according to the principle of superposition, the output of a circuit which is subject to several inputs is the sum of the outputs obtained when each of the inputs is applied successively, the remainder being set to zero. Writing Eq. (2.3) in the form shown in Eq. (2.4), stresses the point that we must seek two parts to the solution, namely the values of v_C which satisfy

$$RC\frac{dv_C}{dt} + v_C = 0 \qquad (2.5)$$

and

$$RC\frac{dv_C}{dt} + v_C = E \qquad (2.6)$$

Eq. (2.6) is identical to Eq. (2.3) and its solution, known as the *particular integral*, or *forced response*, shows how the circuit responds to the particular input or forcing function—in this case the step function rising to E volts d.c. The solution to Eq. (2.5) (which along with other linear differential equations with zero right hand side is called a *homogeneous* equation) is known as the *complementary function*, or the *natural response*. The natural response of all linear circuits has a form which is independent of the input applied to the circuit (in this case a battery of voltage E), although we shall find that its magnitude is influenced by the input in a manner which may be determined from the initial conditions in the circuit. To sum up, the complete response of all linear circuits comprises two parts—the natural response whose form is dictated solely by the circuit components, and the forced response which is related to both the circuit and its input.

To find the natural response, a solution of the form $v_C = Ae^{st}$ may be tried. (This is a safe bet, and works with all linear differential equations with constant coefficients.) It remains to find the unknowns A and s. With this solution, $\frac{dv_C}{dt} = Ase^{st}$, and substituting this in Eq. (2.5):

$$RC \cdot Ase^{st} + Ae^{st} = 0$$

Cancelling Ae^{st}, this gives

$$sRC + 1 = 0, \text{ i.e., } s = \left(\frac{-1}{RC}\right)$$

Thus, $v_C = Ae^{-t/RC}$, with A yet to be determined. Leaving this aside for a moment, and now turning to Eq. (2.6), a solution of the form $v_C = $ constant may be tried in the equation, noting that the input voltage E is constant for $t \geqslant 0$. Then $\left(\frac{dv_C}{dt}\right) = 0$, and Eq. (2.6) gives

$$0 + v_C = E$$

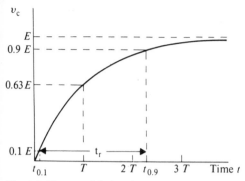

Fig. 2.2 Exponential charging characteristic

The forced response is thus $v_C = E$. From the earlier remarks, the complete response is the sum of the natural and forced responses, that is

$$v_C = Ae^{-t/RC} + E \qquad (2.7)$$

To find A, note that at time $t = 0$, $v_C = 0$, and so in Eq. (2.7)

$$0 = A + E$$

$$\therefore \qquad A = -E$$

Finally we have

$$v_C = E(1 - e^{-t/RC}) \qquad (2.8)$$

Eq. (2.8) expresses the exponential form of the capacitor voltage in a simple RC charging circuit, and this expression is plotted in Fig. 2.2. This graph confirms the reasoned observations which were made earlier.

It will be noted in Eq. (2.8) that since either side of the expression must have the dimensions of volts, the product RC must have the dimension of time, if $e^{-t/RC}$ is to be dimensionless. In fact $T = RC$ is known as the *time constant* of the circuit. After a time $t = T$s, $v_C = E(1 - e^{-1}) = 0.63\,E$, that is the capacitor has attained 63% of its full voltage (or full charge). Evaluating v_C for further times leads to the results tabulated in Table 2.1.

Table 2.1

Time t	v_C	% of full charge
T	$0.63\,E$	63
$2T$	$0.86\,E$	86
$3T$	$0.95\,E$	95
$4T$	$0.98\,E$	98
$5T$	$0.99\,E$	99
$6T$	$0.998\,E$	99.8
$7T$	$0.999\,E$	99.9

While Eq. (2.8) indicates that v_C never reaches E volts in finite time, Table 2.1 shows that after a time equivalent to 5 time constants, v_C is within about 1% of its final voltage, and after 7 time constants it is within 0.1% of the final voltage. These facts are useful in the design of RC charging circuits.

Another way to examine the manner in which the capacitor voltage rises is to calculate the *risetime* of the response. This is often taken to be the time in which the response rises from one tenth to nine tenths of the final value as shown in Fig. 2.2. Using Eq. (2.8) with $T = RC$ we have

$$0.1\,E = E(1 - e^{-t_{0.1}/T}), \quad \text{i.e.,} \quad t_{0.1} = -\,T \ln(0.9)$$

and

$$0.9\,E = E(1 - e^{-t_{0.9}/T}), \quad \text{i.e.,} \quad t_{0.9} = -\,T \ln(0.1)$$

Denoting the risetime by t_r, $t_r = t_{0.9} - t_{0.1} = T \ln(9)$, or to a good approximation $t_r = 2.2T$.

Circuits in which the initial conditions are not zero, and other inputs or forcing functions are applied to them may be dealt with in a similar manner to that described above, as the following example shows.

Example

In the circuit shown in Fig. 2.3, a current source of value $i = 2t\,\mu A$ is switched (by 'unshorting' the current source) at time $t = 0$ s. (Note that this means that at $t = 0$ s, the switch will be opened, and the current will then increase at the rate of $2\,\mu A/s$.) If $R_1 = R_2 = 1\,M\Omega$, and $C = 0.5\,\mu F$, derive an expression for the voltage v_C on the capacitor. Assume that the capacitor is initially charged to +2 volts.

Using KCL:

$$i = i_1 + i_2, \tag{2.9}$$

Applying KVL to the loop formed by R_1, R_2 and C:

$$i_1 R_1 - i_2 R_2 - v_C = 0$$

whence

$$i_1 = \frac{1}{R_1}(i_2 R_2 + v_C) \tag{2.10}$$

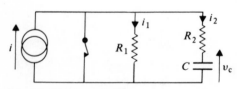

Fig. 2.3 Circuit example

Substituting Eq. (2.10) into Eq. (2.9)

$$i = \frac{1}{R_1}(i_2 R_2 + v_C) + i_2 = i_2\left(1 + \frac{R_2}{R_1}\right) + \frac{1}{R_1}v_C \qquad (2.11)$$

Now for the capacitor $i_2 = C\left(\dfrac{dv_C}{dt}\right)$, and substituting this into Eq. (2.11)

we finally obtain

$$\left(1 + \frac{R_2}{R_1}\right)C\frac{dv_C}{dt} + \frac{1}{R_1}v_C = i$$

With the numerical values given this becomes

$$\left(1 + \frac{10^6}{10^6}\right) \times 0.5 \times 10^{-6}\frac{dv_C}{dt} + \frac{1}{10^6}v_C = 2 \times 10^{-6}t$$

or

$$\frac{dv_C}{dt} + v_C = 2t \qquad (2.12)$$

To find the natural response, as before a solution of the form $v_C = Ae^{st}$ may be substituted into the homogeneous equation

$$\frac{dv_C}{dt} + v_C = 0$$

The reader may care to check that this yields $s = -1$, i.e., $v_C = Ae^{-t}$.

To find the forced response, a solution of the form $v_C = A_1 t + A_0$ may be attempted, the unknown coefficients A_1 and A_0 to be determined. (An indication of the form of solutions for particular cases will be summarized presently.) Thus $(dv_C/dt) = A_1$, and substituting into Eq. (2.12)

$$A_1 + A_1 t + A_0 = 2t$$

i.e.,

$$A_1 t + (A_1 + A_0) = 2t$$

Comparing like powers of t in this last equation, $A_1 = 2$, $A_1 + A_0 = 0$ and so $A_0 = -A_1 = -2$. Combining now the natural and the forced responses,

$$v_C = Ae^{-t} + 2t - 2 \qquad (2.13)$$

We are told that the initial voltage on the capacitor is 2 volts, and therefore since the voltage on a capacitor cannot be changed instantaneously, at time $t = 0$ when the current source is switched on to the circuit, $v_C = 2$ volts. Substituting into Eq. (2.13) for $t = 0$,

$$2 = A + 0 - 2, \text{ i.e., } A = 4$$

The complete solution is therefore

$$v_C = 4e^{-t} + 2t - 2$$

Table 2.2

f(t)	x(t)
$0\dagger$	Ae^{st}
$kt^n (n = 0, 1, 2, \ldots)$	$A_n t^n + A_{n-1} t^{n-1} + \cdots + A_1 t + A_0$
$ke^{\alpha t}$	$Ae^{\alpha t}$
$k \sin \omega t$	$A \sin(\omega t + \phi)$
$k \cos \omega t$	$A \cos(\omega t + \phi)$

$\dagger$This corresponds to the homogeneous equation, whence $x(t)$ is the natural response.

The simplicity in obtaining the solution to the differential equations which describe the circuits considered above is marred only by the need to propose possible solutions. Providing the suggested solutions are realistic, the problems reduce to simple algebra, but it is unfortunately this step which often represents the biggest stumbling block in solving this type of circuit problem. In the majority of cases, it is sufficient to remember only a few rules for the selection of a suitable solution. Thus, given a linear differential equation

$$a_n \frac{d^n x}{dt^n} + a_{n-1} \frac{d^{n-1} x}{dt^{n-1}} + \cdots + a_1 \frac{dx}{dt} + a_0 x = f(t),$$

Table 2.2 summarizes the forms of solution for $x(t)$ which will satisfy the cases of particular forcing functions $f(t)$.

Further application of these rules will be dealt with in the following sections of this and the next chapter.

2.2 RESISTOR–INDUCTOR (RL) CIRCUITS

The inductor is characterized by the differential relationship $v = L\left(\dfrac{di}{dt}\right)$. Using similar reasoning to that applied to the capacitor, it will be seen that *it is impossible to change the current (and hence the flux) in an inductor instantaneously*, since otherwise an infinite $\dfrac{di}{dt}$ would result, or an infinite rate of charge of energy (i.e. power) would be required. Further, an unfluxed inductor (i.e. an inductor passing no initial current) which is connected in a circuit subject to the sudden application of an input at $t = 0$ s will pass no current at the instant of application. Although a voltage may appear across the inductor at that instant, no instantaneous current will flow. Thus, *at $t = 0$ s an inductor behaves as an open circuit*. On the other hand, if a constant current passes through the inductor, $\frac{di}{dt} = 0$ and so $v = 0$. So *an inductor behaves as a short circuit when it passes a constant current*. Armed with these observations, we may now turn to consider the simple circuit shown in Fig. 2.4.

Here, a constant current I will be applied to an unfluxed inductor and a resistor connected in parallel by opening the switch at time $t = 0$ s. From our observations, the current in the inductor will remain zero at $t = 0$, and all the current from the source must therefore flow into the resistor, and so initially, $v = IR$. This voltage will establish a rate of change of current in the inductor, since $v = L\left(\frac{di_L}{dt}\right)$, and i_L will therefore increase. As this happens, less current will flow in the resistor (because the total current in the resistor and inductor is fixed by the constant current source) and so v will decrease. It would seem reasonable to expect this behaviour to continue, until all the current I flows in the inductor, when v will be zero, the inductor then behaving as a short circuit.

This qualitative argument may now be confirmed quantitatively as follows. KCL gives

$$I = \frac{v}{R} + i_L$$

But $v = L(di_L/dt)$, and so

$$\frac{L}{R}\frac{di_L}{dt} + i_L = I \tag{2.14}$$

Eq. (2.14) is of exactly the same form as Eq. (2.3), and so its solution will be similar to Eq. (2.8), and is, in fact

$$i_L = I(1 - e^{-Rt/L}) \tag{2.15}$$

Eq. (2.15) is represented graphically in Fig. 2.5. In this case, the time constant is seen from Eq. (2.15) to be given by $T = \frac{L}{R}$ and the right hand column in Table 2.1 may again be used to estimate the current in the inductor after times corresponding to multiples of time constants. To find

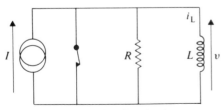

Fig. 2.4 Simple RL charging circuit

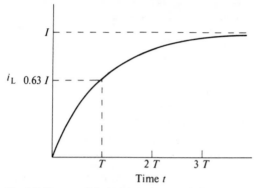

Fig. 2.5 Exponential charging characteristic

the voltage across the inductor, we need only differentiate Eq. (2.15):

$$\frac{di_L}{dt} = I \cdot \frac{R}{L} e^{-Rt/L}$$

$\therefore$

$$v = L \frac{di_L}{dt} = IRe^{-Rt/L} \qquad (2.16)$$

By letting $t = 0$ and $t \to \infty$ in Eq. (2.15) and Eq. (2.16), the earlier qualitative arguments are indeed confirmed.

Example

A flux is arranged to cut the turns of the inductor in the circuit of Fig. 2.6 so that at time $t = 0$ s, it carries an initial current $i_0 = 0.5$ A. A voltage $v_1 = 2t$ is applied to the circuit at that time. If $R_1 = 10\,\Omega$, $R_2 = 20\,\Omega$, and $L = 10$ H, find the resulting voltage v_2 which is established across the series connection of R_2 and L.

The voltage v_2 is the sum of the voltages across R_2 and L, that is

$$v_2 = iR_2 + L \frac{di}{dt}.$$

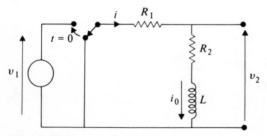

Fig. 2.6 Circuit example

Also

$$i = \frac{v_1 - v_2}{R_1}$$

and so

$$v_2 = R_2 \frac{(v_1 - v_2)}{R_1} + \frac{L}{R_1} \frac{d}{dt}(v_1 - v_2)$$

Collecting terms in v_2 on the left hand side,

$$\frac{L}{R_1}\frac{dv_2}{dt} + v_2\left(1 + \frac{R_2}{R_1}\right) = \frac{L}{R_1}\frac{dv_1}{dt} + \frac{R_2}{R_1}v_1 \qquad (2.17)$$

If the component values are inserted, Eq. (2.17) becomes

$$\frac{10}{10}\frac{dv_2}{dt} + v_2\left(1 + \frac{20}{10}\right) = \left(\frac{10}{10} \cdot 2\right) + \left(\frac{20}{10} \cdot 2t\right)$$

i.e.,

$$\frac{dv_2}{dt} + 3v_2 = 4t + 2 \qquad (2.18)$$

Having obtained the differential equation, we can now proceed to its solution in the usual way. The natural response is obtained from the homogeneous equation

$$\frac{dv_2}{dt} + 3v_2 = 0$$

It should be clear from the previous examples that this equation has the solution $v_2 = Ae^{-3t}$, the unknown coefficient A yet to be determined from the initial conditions. Now for the forced response. Eq. (2.18) differs from the cases which were considered previously in that there are two terms on the right hand side. However, Eq. (2.18) is a linear differential equation (since it has been obtained from a linear circuit), and the principle of superposition applies. In other words, we can consider each of the terms in Eq. (2.18) to be separate forcing functions for the *equation* (rather than for the circuit), find the solution to each, and combine these solutions to obtain the forced response. First we may take

$$\frac{dv_2}{dt} + 3v_2 = 4t \qquad (2.19)$$

and referring to Table 2.2, propose a solution $v_2 = A_1t + A_0$. Substituting into Eq. (2.19):

$$A_1 + 3(A_1t + A_0) = 4t$$

i.e.,

$$3A_1 = 4 \quad \therefore \ A_1 = \frac{4}{3}$$

$$A_1 + 3A_0 = 0 \quad \therefore \ A_0 = -\frac{1}{3} A_1 = -\frac{4}{9}$$

$$\therefore \ v_2 = \frac{4}{3} t - \frac{4}{9}$$

Now we take

$$\frac{\mathrm{d}v_2}{\mathrm{d}t} + 3v_2 = 2 \tag{2.20}$$

In this case $v_2 = $ constant may be substituted in Eq. (2.20), giving:

$$0 + 3v_2 = 2, \ i.e., \ v_2 = \frac{2}{3}$$

The forced response is therefore

$$v_2 = \frac{4}{3} t - \frac{4}{9} + \frac{2}{3} = \frac{4}{3} t + \frac{2}{9}$$

The reader may care to substitute this solution into Eq. (2.18) to confirm that it is indeed the forced response.

The complete response of the circuit is the sum of the natural and forced responses, and is

$$v_2 = A e^{-3t} + \frac{4}{3} t + \frac{2}{9} \tag{2.21}$$

Now at time $t = 0$, the inductor carries an initial current of 0.5 A in the direction shown in Fig. 2.6. Thus, at $t = 0$, $i = i_0$, and so $v_2 = v_1 - i_0 R_1 = 2 \times 0 - 0.5 \times 10 = -5$ volts. Setting $t = 0$ in Eq. (2.21), this gives

$$-5 = A + \frac{2}{9}, \quad i.e., \ A = -\frac{47}{9}$$

Finally therefore, the complete solution for the circuit is:

$$v_2 = -\frac{47}{9} e^{-3t} + \frac{4}{3} t + \frac{2}{9}$$

2.3 RESISTOR–INDUCTOR–CAPACITOR (RLC) CIRCUITS

In the previous two sections attention was concentrated on the behaviour of circuits containing resistors together with one capacitor or inductor. In this section, the behaviour of circuits containing both a capacitor and an inductor will be considered. In common with the simple RC and RL circuits, such LCR circuits are of great importance, since they occur in many practical situations.

In the circuit of Fig. 2.7, a battery of voltage E is to be applied to the series RLC circuit at time $t = 0$ s. Assuming that the inductor and capacitor are initially unfluxed and uncharged respectively, we seek the resulting voltage v_C across the capacitor.

At the instant of closing the switch, the inductor will behave as an open circuit, and so the initial value of the current i shown in Fig. 2.7 must be zero. Also at that instant, the capacitor will behave as a short circuit, and so initially v_C will be zero. As time tends to infinity, if a constant voltage is established across the capacitor, no current will flow through it, since it will then behave as an open circuit. Since that current is i, the voltage drop across the inductor (which will behave as a short circuit, even though the constant current through it actually has a value of zero) and the resistor will be zero, and so we see that the constant value of v_C which we assumed will in fact be $v_C = E$. To sum up, these simple observations indicate that v_C will start at zero, and as time extends to infinity, it will reach E volts in some way.

Considering the inductor and resistor, KVL gives

$$E = L\frac{di}{dt} + iR + v_C \tag{2.22}$$

while for the capacitor,

$$i = C\frac{dv_C}{dt} \tag{2.23}$$

and therefore

$$\frac{di}{dt} = C\frac{d^2v_C}{dt^2} \tag{2.24}$$

Substituting Eq. (2.23) and Eq. (2.24) in Eq. (2.22):

$$LC\frac{d^2v_C}{dt^2} + RC\frac{dv_C}{dt} + v_C = E \tag{2.25}$$

Eq. (2.25) shows that in this case a second order differential equation

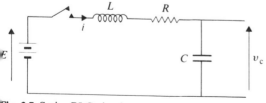

Fig. 2.7 Series RLC circuit

characterizes the behaviour of the circuit. We may find its solution in exactly the same way as before. Taking the homogeneous equation

$$LC\frac{d^2v_C}{dt^2} + RC\frac{dv_C}{dt} + v_C = 0 \qquad (2.26)$$

the solution $v_C = Ae^{st}$ may be substituted for the natural response. Thus,

$$\frac{dv_C}{dt} = sAe^{st}, \quad \frac{d^2v_C}{dt^2} = s^2Ae^{st},$$

and Eq. (2.26) becomes

$$LCs^2Ae^{st} + RCsAe^{st} + Ae^{st} = 0$$

i.e.,

$$s^2LC + sRC + 1 = 0 \qquad (2.27)$$

Eq. (2.27) is quadratic which indicates that two values of s will satisfy the natural response. We must take account of both of them, so solving Eq. (2.27),

$$s = \frac{-RC \pm [(RC)^2 - 4LC]^{1/2}}{2LC} = -\frac{R}{2L} \pm \left[\left(\frac{R}{2L}\right)^2 - \frac{1}{LC}\right]^{1/2} \qquad (2.28)$$

or

$$s_1 = a + b^{1/2} \qquad (2.29)$$

$$s_2 = a - b^{1/2} \qquad (2.30)$$

where for clarity a and b have been defined as

$$a = -\frac{R}{2L} \qquad (2.31)$$

$$b = \left(\frac{R}{2L}\right)^2 - \frac{1}{LC} \qquad (2.32)$$

The natural response must therefore be written as

$$v_C = A_1e^{s_1t} + A_2e^{s_2t}$$

to take account to these two solutions, and as always, the unknown coefficients A_1 and A_2 have yet to be determined from the initial conditions.

Returning to Eq. (2.25), the forced response may be found by suggesting that v_C is constant, and thus

$$LC \times 0 + RC \times 0 + v_C = E$$

i.e.,

$$v_C = E$$

The complete solution for the circuit is therefore

$$v_C = A_1 e^{s_1 t} + A_2 e^{s_2 t} + E \tag{2.33}$$

To find A_1 and A_2, note that $v_C = 0$ at time $t = 0$ s. At this time, Eq. (2.33) gives

$$0 = A_1 + A_2 + E \tag{2.34}$$

Another equation is needed before A_1 and A_2 can be found. This equation is obtained by recalling the earlier remark that i will be zero at time $t = 0$ s, and Eq. (2.23) shows that $\dfrac{dv_C}{dt}$ will therefore be zero at that time. So, differentiating Eq. (2.33):

$$\frac{dv_C}{dt} = A_1 s_1 e^{s_1 t} + A_2 s_2 e^{s_2 t}$$

and substituting for $t = 0$,

$$0 = A_1 s_1 + A_2 s_2 \tag{2.35}$$

Eq. (2.34) and Eq. (2.35) are two simultaneous equations in A_1 and A_2 which may be simply solved to yield

$$A_1 = \frac{s_2 E}{s_1 - s_2}; \quad A_2 = \frac{-s_1 E}{s_1 - s_2}$$

and so the complete solution (Eq. (2.33)) becomes

$$v_c = E\left(\frac{s_2 e^{s_1 t} - s_1 e^{s_2 t}}{s_1 - s_2}\right) + E \tag{2.36}$$

Although the complete response has now been derived, this is far from the end of the story as far as this circuit is concerned, for the precise form of the solution will depend on the nature of s_1 and s_2. In particular, the magnitude of $\left(\dfrac{R}{2L}\right)^2$ compared with $\dfrac{1}{LC}$ in Eq. (2.28) will decide whether in Eq. (2.29) and Eq. (2.30) is positive, zero, or negative. These three cases will now be considered in turn.

$$\left(\frac{R}{2L}\right)^2 > \frac{1}{LC}$$

This case is simply dealt with, and merely requires the straightforward substitution of values of s_1 and s_2 in Eq. (2.36). For example, if $R = 4\,\text{k}\Omega$, $L = 0.5\,\text{H}$ and $C = 0.4\,\mu\text{F}$ and $E = 1$ volt, Eq. (2.28)–(2.32) give

$$s_1 = -\frac{4 \times 10^3}{2 \times 0.5} + \left[\left(\frac{4 \times 10^3}{2 \times 0.5}\right)^2 - \frac{1}{0.5 \times 0.4 \times 10^{-6}}\right]^{1/2}$$

$$= -4 \times 10^3 + [16 \times 10^6 - 5 \times 10^6]^{1/2} = -10^3$$

and similarly, $s_2 = -7 \times 10^3$.

Inserting these values in Eq. (2.36), we have

$$v_C = \left(\frac{-7 \times 10^3 e^{-10^3 t} + 10^3 e^{-7 \times 10^3 t}}{-10^3 - (-7 \times 10^3)}\right) + 1$$

i.e.,

$$v_C = 1 - \frac{7}{6} e^{-10^3 t} + \frac{1}{6} e^{-7 \times 10^3 t} \tag{2.3?}$$

Eq. (2.37) is plotted as curve (a) in Fig. 2.8.

(ii) $$\left(\frac{R}{2L}\right)^2 = \frac{1}{LC}$$

Eq. (2.32) together with Eq. (2.28) and Eq. (2.30) show that the conditio $\left(\frac{R}{2L}\right)^2 = \frac{1}{LC}$ make $b = 0$, and more important, $s_1 = s_2$. However, $s_1 = s_2$ is substituted in Eq. (2.36), it becomes

$$v_C = E\left(\frac{0}{0}\right) + E$$

which is apparently indeterminate. This dilemma may be resolved b involving L'Hopital's rule. In general terms, L'Hopital's rule states tha given a function $f(x) = \frac{g(x)}{h(x)}$, such that with $x \to a$, $g(a) \to 0$ and $h(a) \to 0$, $f(a$ is given by $f(a) = \left(\frac{g'(x)}{h'(x)}\right)_{x=a}$, where the primes denote differentiation wit respect to the variable x. For the case in hand, selecting s_2 as the variabl the application of L'Hopital's rule to Eq. (2.36) gives

$$v_C = E\left(\frac{e^{s_1 t} - s_1 t e^{s_2 t}}{-1}\right)_{s_2 = s_1} + E$$

i.e.,

$$v_C = E e^{s_1 t}(s_1 t - 1) + E \tag{2.3?}$$

Again, selecting $R = 4\,k\Omega$, $L = 0.5\,H$, $E = 1$ volt, but now with C 0.125 μF, Eq. (2.31) and Eq. (2.32) give

$$a = \frac{-4 \times 10^3}{2 \times 0.5} = -4 \times 10^3$$

and

$$b = \left(\frac{4 \times 10^3}{2 \times 0.5}\right)^2 - \frac{1}{0.5 \times 0.125 \times 10^{-6}} = 0$$

Eq. (2.38) therefore applies, and substituting $s_1 = -4 \times 10^3$ this becomes

$$v_C = 1 - e^{-4 \times 10^3 t}(4 \times 10^3 t + 1) \tag{2.39}$$

q. (2.39) is plotted as curve (b) in Fig. 2.8.

ii)
$$\left(\frac{R}{2L}\right)^2 < \frac{1}{LC}$$

This case causes some difficulty, since Eq. (2.32) shows that b will be egative, and so $b^{1/2}$ in Eq. (2.29) and Eq. (2.30) will be imaginary. To see ae implication of this, we may substitute Eq. (2.29) and Eq. (2.30) into Eq. 2.36). This gives:

$$v_C = E\left[\frac{(a - b^{1/2})e^{(a+b^{1/2})t} - (a + b^{1/2})e^{(a-b^{1/2})t}}{(a + b^{1/2}) - (a - b^{1/2})}\right] + E$$

Taking out the factor e^{at}, and rearranging, this becomes

$$v_C = E - \frac{Ee^{at}}{2b^{1/2}}[b^{1/2}(e^{b^{1/2}t} + e^{-b^{1/2}t}) - a(e^{b^{1/2}t} - e^{-b^{1/2}t})] \tag{2.40}$$

The difficulty in Eq. (2.40) lies in the interpretation of the quantities $b^{1/2}$, nd $e^{b^{1/2}t}$ and $e^{-b^{1/2}t}$. One approach to the simplification of Eq. (2.40) is hrough the use of complex numbers (which are discussed in Chapter 3). Iowever, it will be shown that an alternative approach will readily satisfy our needs.

Consider the term $(e^{b^{1/2}t} + e^{-b^{1/2}t})$ in Eq. (2.40). Now the series expansions or the two exponentials are

$$e^{b^{1/2}t} = 1 + (b^{1/2}t) + \frac{(b^{1/2}t)^2}{2!} + \frac{(b^{1/2}t)^3}{3!} + \frac{(b^{1/2}t)^4}{4!} \cdots \cdots \tag{2.41}$$

$$e^{-b^{1/2}t} = 1 - (b^{1/2}t) + \frac{(b^{1/2}t)^2}{2!} - \frac{(b^{1/2}t)^3}{3!} + \frac{(b^{1/2}t)^4}{4!} \cdots \cdots \tag{2.42}$$

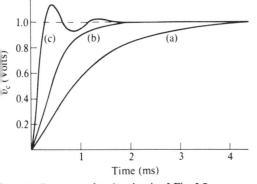

Fig. 2.8 Responses for the circuit of Fig. 2.7

Adding Eq. (2.41) and Eq. (2.42) we have

$$e^{b^{1/2}t} + e^{-b^{1/2}t} = 2\left[1 + \frac{(b^{1/2}t)^2}{2!} + \frac{(b^{1/2}t)^4}{4!} + \frac{(b^{1/2}t)^6}{6!} + \cdots\cdots\right]$$

$$= 2\left[1 + \frac{bt^2}{2!} + \frac{b^2t^4}{4!} + \frac{b^3t^6}{6!} + \cdots\cdots\right] \qquad (2.4?)$$

Eq. (2.43) is most satisfactory, because it contains no terms in $b^{1/2}$. The fac? that b is negative may now be stressed by setting $b = -c$, where c i? positive, that is

$$c = \frac{1}{LC} - \left(\frac{R}{2L}\right)^2 \qquad (2.44?)$$

Rewriting Eq. (2.43):

$$e^{b^{1/2}t} + e^{-b^{1/2}t} = 2\left[1 - \frac{(c^{1/2}t)^2}{2!} + \frac{(c^{1/2}t)^4}{4!} - \frac{(c^{1/2}t)^6}{6!} + \cdots\cdots\right] \qquad (2.45?)$$

The series on the right hand side of Eq. (2.45) may be recognised as the? expansion of $\cos(c^{1/2}t)$, and so

$$e^{b^{1/2}t} + e^{-b^{1/2}t} = 2\cos(c^{1/2}t) \qquad (2.46?)$$

Differentiating both sides of Eq. (2.46) with respect to time,

$$b^{1/2}e^{b^{1/2}t} - b^{1/2}e^{-b^{1/2}t} = -2c^{1/2}\sin(c^{1/2}t)$$

i.e.,

$$e^{b^{1/2}t} - e^{-b^{1/2}t} = -\frac{2c^{1/2}}{b^{1/2}}\sin(c^{1/2}t) \qquad (2.47?)$$

This last equation identifies the second term in Eq. (2.40). Substituting? Eq. (2.46) and Eq. (2.47) into Eq. (2.40)

$$v_c = E - \frac{Ee^{at}}{2b^{1/2}}\left[2b^{1/2}\cos(c^{1/2}t) + \frac{2ac^{1/2}}{b^{1/2}}\sin(c^{1/2}t)\right]$$

i.e.,

$$v_c = E - \frac{Ee^{at}}{c}\left[c\cos(c^{1/2}t) - ac^{1/2}\sin(c^{1/2}t)\right] \qquad (2.48)$$

This last equation shows that the difficulties regarding b have been overcome. It will be noted that in this case the response includes an oscillatory term, the frequency of oscillation being

$$c^{1/2} = \left[\frac{1}{LC} - \left(\frac{R}{2L}\right)^2\right]^{1/2} \text{ rad/s}$$

Taking the same values as before ($R = 4\,k\Omega$, $L = 0.5\,H$, $E = 1$ volt), but now with $C = 0.03\,\mu F$, we have from Eq. (2.44)

$$c = \frac{1}{0.5 \times 0.03 \times 10^{-6}} - \left(\frac{4 \times 10^3}{2 \times 0.5}\right)^2 = 66.7 \times 10^6 - 16 \times 10^6 = 50.7 \times 10^6$$

and as before

$$a = -4 \times 10^3$$

Eq. (2.48) then becomes

$$v_c = 1 - \frac{e^{-4 \times 10^3 t}}{50.7 \times 10^6} [50.7 \times 10^6 \cos (7.1 \times 10^3 t) + 28.5 \times 10^6 \sin (7.1 \times 10^3 t)]$$

$$= 1 - e^{-4 \times 10^3 t} [\cos (7.1 \times 10^3 t) + 0.56 \sin (7.1 \times 10^3 t)] \qquad (2.49)$$

Eq. (2.49) is displayed graphically as curve (c) in Fig. 2.8.

While the graphs in Fig. 2.8 have been drawn for specific component values in the circuit of Fig. 2.7, they are indicative of the types of responses obtained in the three cases discussed above. Curve (a), corresponding to $\left(\frac{R}{2L}\right)^2 > \frac{1}{LC}$ is said to be an *overdamped* response, since it rises to the final value more slowly than the other two cases. However, there is no oscillatory behaviour leading to overshoots as seen in curve (c). When $\left(\frac{R}{2L}\right)^2 = \frac{1}{LC}$, curve (b) shows that the response rises faster than the overdamped response, but again has no overshoots. This response is said to be *critically damped*, and it may be shown that it corresponds to the shortest risetime which may be achieved without overshooting the final value. Finally, curve (c) which exhibits overshoots and oscillation about the final value is said to be *underdamped*. Such a response is often said to be *ringing*, this term indicating that some oscillation is present in the response.

Example

For the circuit shown in Fig. 2.9, find the conditions under which the response v_2 will be overdamped, critically damped, and underdamped.

Note that we are told nothing about v_1 in this problem. However, this is

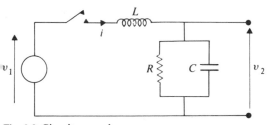

Fig. 2.9 Circuit example

of no importance, since the conditions for examining damping are obtained from the homogeneous differential equation, as we have seen.

Assuming a current i flows when the switch is closed, then inspection of the circuit reveals:

$$v_1 - v_2 = L\frac{di}{dt} \quad and \quad i = \frac{v_2}{R} + C\frac{dv_2}{dt}$$

Eliminating i between these equations,

$$v_1 - v_2 = \frac{L}{R}\frac{dv_2}{dt} + LC\frac{d^2v_2}{dt^2}$$

i.e.,

$$LC\frac{d^2v_2}{dt^2} + \frac{L}{R}\frac{dv_2}{dt} + v_2 = v_1 \tag{2.50}$$

Taking the homogeneous equation from Eq. (2.50), and substituting $v_2 = Ae^{st}$ as usual, we obtain

$$s^2 LC + s\frac{L}{R} + 1 = 0$$

The two values of s are then given by:

$$s = \frac{-\dfrac{L}{R} \pm \left[\left(\dfrac{L}{R}\right)^2 - 4LC\right]^{1/2}}{2LC} = -\frac{1}{2RC} \pm \left[\frac{1}{(2RC)^2} - \frac{1}{LC}\right]^{1/2}$$

Thus, the response will be overdamped when $\frac{1}{(2RC)^2} > \frac{1}{LC}$, critically damped when $\frac{1}{(2RC)^2} = \frac{1}{LC}$, and underdamped when $\frac{1}{(2RC)^2} < \frac{1}{LC}$, since in each case the term $\left[\frac{1}{(2RC)^2} - \frac{1}{LC}\right]$ will be positive, zero and negative respectively.

2.4 FURTHER FORCING FUNCTIONS

The techniques of time domain analysis treated in the previous sections are generally applicable to a wide range of circuits. If the number of capacitors and inductors in the circuit exceeds two, the order of the differential equation may well require the use of a digital computer to solve the polynomial in s obtained from the homogeneous equation, but the approach is otherwise just the same. The major difficulty occurs when the forcing functions or inputs to the circuit are more complex than those dealt with in the previous sections. However, the principle of superposition is frequently useful here, as the following examples will show.

Figure 2.10(a) shows the output voltage of an ideal source which is to be applied to a circuit. This voltage may clearly be represented as the sum of the two voltages shown in Fig. 2.10(b). By considering each voltage as a separate forcing function in turn, the principle of superposition may then be invoked to give the composite forced response. The application of this technique to other waveforms is obvious. For example, consider the pulse

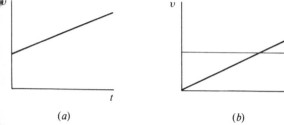

(a)   (b)

Fig. 2.10 Decomposition of a complex waveform

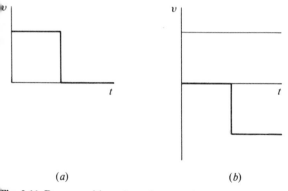

(a)   (b)

Fig. 2.11 Decomposition of a pulse waveform

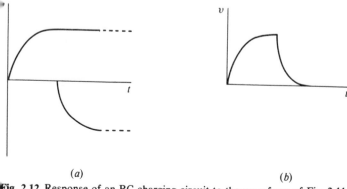

(a)   (b)

Fig. 2.12 Response of an RC charging circuit to the waveform of Fig. 2.11

shown in Fig. 2.11(a). This may be decomposed into two step functions as shown in Fig. 2.11(b).

If these two voltages were applied to the simple RC charging circuit considered in section 2.1, the waveforms shown in Fig. 2.12(a) might result. Superimposing these two waveforms, we arrive at Fig. 2.12(b), which therefore represents the response to the input waveform shown in Fig. 2.11(a). This procedure is readily extendable to the case of repetitive waveforms.

2.5 SUMMARY

In this chapter, we have considered the time domain analysis of linear circuits. The transient response has been found by solving the linear differential equations characterising the circuits. The response consists of two parts: the forced response which corresponds to the particular forcing function or input applied to the circuit, and the natural response, whose form depends solely on the circuit, but whose magnitude depends on the input and the initial conditions. These initial conditions may often be obtained by inspection of the circuit, after consideration of the behaviour of capacitors and inductors when subjected to both sudden changes and constant values of voltage or current applied to their terminals.

CHAPTER 2

Problems

1. Find the initial and final values for the voltage $v_0(t)$ in the circuit shown in Fig. 2.13 when a d.c. voltage $v_{in} = 1$ volt is applied at time $t = 0$ s.
   $\left(\text{Answer: } \frac{3}{7}\,\text{V}, \frac{3}{4}\,\text{V}\right)$

2. Calculate the voltage $v_0(t)$ in the circuit of Fig. 2.14 when a 2 volt step is applied to the input at time $t = 0$ s. The capacitor is initially uncharged.
   (Answer: $v_0(t) = 2 - 1.5e^{-t/4}$)

3. Capacitor C_1 in Fig. 2.15 is charged to E volts. At time $t = 0$ s, the switch is closed. Determine the resulting current i.
   $\left(\text{Answer: } \frac{E}{R}\exp\left[-\frac{(C_1 + C_2)t}{C_1 C_2 R}\right]\right)$

4. The current source in Fig. 2.16 supplies a current $i(t) = \begin{cases} 0, & t \leq 0 \\ t, & t > 0 \end{cases}$
   Find the voltage $v_0(t)$.
   (Answer: $v_0(t) = 10^{-3}(1 - e^{-10^7 t})$)

5. Two inductors, $L_1 = 0.4\,\text{H}$ and $L_2 = 1.6\,\text{H}$, are coupled, with coupling coefficient $k = 0.5$. The inductors are connected as shown in Fig. 2.17. If the battery is switched on to the circuit at time $t = 0$ s, find the resulting voltage across the resistor.
   (Answer: $1 - e^{-50t}$ volts)

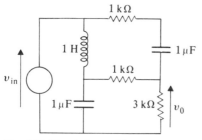

Fig. 2.13 Circuit for problem 1

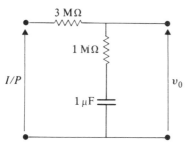

Fig. 2.14 Circuit for problem 2

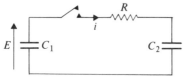

Fig. 2.15 RC circuit for problem 3

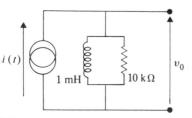

Fig. 2.16 RL circuit (problem 4)

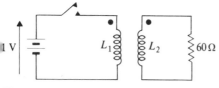

Fig. 2.17 Coupled inductors (problem 5)

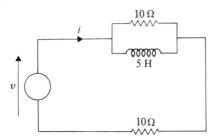

Fig. 2.18 RL circuit (problem 6)

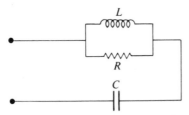

Fig. 2.19 LCR circuit for problem 7

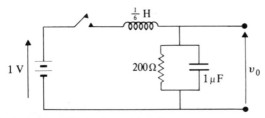

Fig. 2.20 LCR circuit (problem 8)

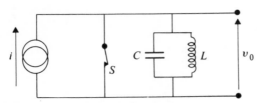

Fig. 2.21 LC circuit for problem 9

6. A voltage $v = \begin{cases} 0, & t<0 \\ e^{-2t}, & t \geq 0 \end{cases}$ is applied to the circuit shown in Fig. 2.18. Calculate the resulting current flow.
   (Answer: $0.05e^{-t}$ A)
7. Find the conditions for the circuit shown in Fig. 2.19 to have a critically damped response when driven with a voltage step.
   (Answer: $L = 4CR^2$)
8. Determine the output voltage $v_0(t)$ if the battery is switched onto the circuit shown in Fig. 2.20 at time $t = 0$ s.
   (Answer: $v_0(t) = 1 - 3e^{-2 \times 10^3 t} + 2e^{-3 \times 10^3 t}$)

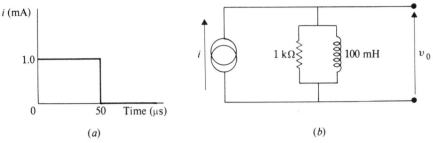

Fig. 2.22 (*a*) Source waveform, (*b*) circuit for problem 10

9. Calculate the output voltage $v_0(t)$ in Fig. 2.21 if $i = I_m \sin \omega t$, and the switch S is opened at time $t = 0$ s.

$$\left(\text{Answer: } v_0(t) = \frac{\omega L I_m}{1 - \omega^2 LC} \left[\cos \omega t - \cos (t/\sqrt{LC}) \right] \right)$$

10. A pulse of current indicated by Fig. 2.22(a) is applied to the circuit in Fig. 2.22(b). Determine the output voltage v_0 at $t = 75 \, \mu$s.
(Answer: -0.31 V)

3

FREQUENCY DOMAIN CIRCUIT ANALYSIS

In this chapter we shall be concerned with the analysis of circuits having input signals which vary sinusoidally with time. Sinusoidal or sinewave signals are of great importance in electronics, one of their particular properties being that if such a signal is applied to a linear circuit of any complexity, and providing the circuit is left for a long enough time to reach a steady state, then all the voltages and currents around the circuit will also be varying sinusoidally at the same frequency as the input. Each voltage or current sinusoid will have an amplitude determined by the circuit configuration, and some time displacement or phase shift with respect to the input. In the analysis of circuits with sinusoidal inputs, the time varying behaviour of the circuit voltages and currents may therefore be put to one side, (it being implicitly understood that they are sinusoids), and attention can concentrate on the calculation of these amplitudes and phases. Since these will in general be functions of the frequency of the input signal, such analysis is said to be conducted in the *frequency domain*.

To explore this idea, we shall follow through the solution of a differential equation describing the behaviour of a circuit having a sinusoidal input signal, and note the mathematical complexity of this approach. However, by appreciating that the sinusoidal steady-state voltages and currents in a circuit are characterised by their amplitudes and phases, and by interpreting these as magnitudes and directions respectively, we shall see that the voltages and currents may be represented by vectors. It is this representation which will be shown to simplify the analysis of circuits in the frequency domain—that is, the calculation of their *sinusoidal response.*

3.1 THE SINEWAVE FORCING FUNCTION

The importance of the sinewave in electrical engineering is readily appreciated by noting that with the exception of one or two d.c. installations, all the power generation authorities the world over provide low frequency sinusoidal mains supplies. In the telecommunications field, many radio and line communications links are effected by impressing information on, or modulating sinusoidal carrier signals generated in the transmitter, and then demodulating or detecting these signals, often through the use of sinusoidal oscillators within the receiver. The sinewave oscillator also holds a prominent position as a piece of test equipment in the electronics laboratory.

The wide practical use of sinusoids has not resulted accidentally, but because sinusoidal voltages are relatively easy to generate, and have therefore always been of great interest to engineers.

From a circuit theory point of view, sinusoids have important mathematical properties. For example consider a voltage given by

$$v = V_p \sin \omega t \tag{3.1}$$

Here, V_p volts is the peak value, or amplitude of the sinewave, and ω rad/s is its frequency. We shall now consider some basic mathematical operations on expressions of the type given in Eq. (3.1). Differentiating Eq. (3.1) with respect to time, we obtain

$$\frac{dv}{dt} = \omega V_p \cos \omega t$$

i.e.,

$$\frac{dv}{dt} = \omega V_p \sin \left(\omega t + \frac{\pi}{2} \right) \tag{3.2}$$

The differentiation of a sinewave with respect to time results in a sinewave, but as Eq. (3.2) shows, this has an amplitude of ωV_p volts/second and a phase shift of $\frac{\pi}{2}$ radians with respect to v. Fig. 3.1 shows the sinusoid corresponding to $\frac{dv}{dt}$ superimposed on a graph of v against time to show the effect of this phase shift.

The phase shift of $\frac{dv}{dt}$ with respect to v is said to be 'leading' by $\frac{\pi}{2}$ radians, which may be interpreted as meaning that $\frac{dv}{dt}$ reaches its positive maximum $\frac{\pi}{2}$ radians before v.

Integrating Eq. (3.1) with respect to time, we have

$$\int v \, dt = -\frac{V_p}{\omega} \cos \omega t$$

i.e.,

$$\int v \, dt = \frac{V_p}{\omega} \sin \left(\omega t - \frac{\pi}{2} \right) \tag{3.3}$$

Eq. (3.3) shows that integration of a sinewave also leads to a sinewave, the amplitude and phase shift being V_p/ω volt-seconds and $\frac{-\pi}{2}$ radians respectively. In this case $\int v \, dt$ is said to 'lag' v by $\frac{\pi}{2}$ radians, this being shown in Fig. 3.2.

The algebraic summation of sinewaves of the same frequency also leads

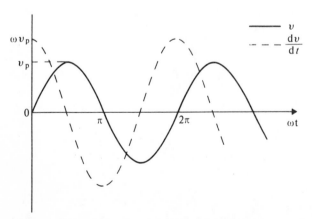

Fig. 3.1 Differentiation of a sinusoidal signal with respect to time

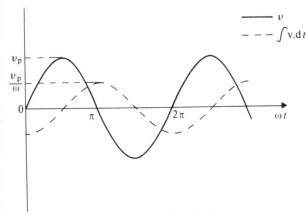

Fig. 3.2 Time intergral of a sinusoidal signal

to a similar result. For example, if we have

$$v = A \sin \omega t + B \sin (\omega t + \phi)$$

where one sinusoidal component has a phase shift of ϕ radians with respect to the other, then straightforward expansion gives

$$v = A \sin \omega t + B \cos \phi \sin \omega t + B \sin \phi \cos \omega t$$
$$= (A + B \cos \phi) \sin \omega t + B \sin \phi \cos \omega t$$

This last equation may now be written as

$$v = [(A + B \cos \phi)^2 + B^2 \sin^2 \phi]^{1/2} \left\{ \frac{A + B \cos \phi}{[(A + B \cos \phi)^2 + B^2 \sin^2 \phi]^{1/2}} \right.$$
$$\left. \sin \omega t + \frac{B \sin \phi}{[(A + B \cos \phi)^2 + B^2 \sin^2 \phi]^{1/2}} \cos \omega t \right\}$$

With reference to Fig. 3.3, we may now set

$$\cos \theta = \frac{A + B \cos \phi}{[(A + B \cos \phi)^2 + B^2 \sin^2 \phi]^{1/2}}; \sin \theta = \frac{B \sin \phi}{[(A + B \cos \phi)^2 + B^2 \sin^2 \phi]^{1/2}}$$

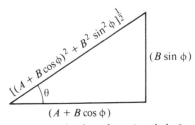

Fig. 3.3 Derivation of $\cos \theta$ and $\sin \theta$

Finally, we see that we may write

$$v = V_p \sin(\omega t + \phi)$$

with

$$V_p = [(A + B \cos \phi)^2 + B^2 \sin^2 \phi]^{1/2}$$

$$\theta = \tan^{-1} \left[\frac{B \sin \phi}{A + B \cos \phi} \right]$$

The phase shift of v with respect to $A \sin \omega t$ will be leading or lagging according to whether θ is positive or negative respectively.

We see therefore that the mathematical operations of differentiation, integration and summation leave the sinusoidal nature of voltages (and in the same way, currents) unchanged. In linear circuits, it is the capacitors and inductors which effectively perform the operations of differentiation and integration, while Kirchhoff's voltage and current laws govern the summation of voltages and currents around the circuit. With this knowledge, we intuitively expect that all voltages and currents in a linear circuit driven with a sinusoidal input will therefore be sinusoids, or at least have a sinusoidal component.

In the electronics laboratory, circuits are often tested by driving them with a sinusoidal voltage from a signal generator, and observing the nature of the resulting output. Any deviation of the output signal from a pure sinusoid indicates that the circuit is not linear, and is the basis for the assessment of distortion–distortion measuring sets use this technique. Furthermore, we shall see later in Chapter 8 that it is possible to represent any periodic signal as a sum of harmonically related sinusoids, (that is, having a frequency which is an integer multiple of the fundamental frequency of the periodic signal), together with a d.c. component, and so armed with the principle of superposition, a knowledge of the amplitude and phase of the output signal for each harmonic frequency is one way of assessing the performance of a circuit when driven by a periodic signal having any waveform. The manner in which this amplitude and phase change with frequency is known as the *frequency response*, a topic which we shall study later. For the time being, having established the importance of the sinusoid, we may now turn our attention to consider the simple circuit shown in Fig. 3.4.

We are interested in finding the output voltage v, developed across the capacitor, when an input voltage $v_{in} = V_p \sin \omega t$ is applied at time $t = 0$. We shall assume that the capacitor C is initially uncharged, and inductor L is unfluxed.

Invoking Kirchhoff's Voltage Law:

$$v_{in} = Ri + L \frac{di}{dt} + v \tag{3.4}$$

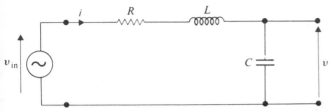

Fig. 3.4 Circuit example

with

$$i = C \frac{dv}{dt} \tag{3.5}$$

and so by substituting Eq. (3.5) into Eq. (3.4) and rearranging, we have

$$LC \frac{d^2v}{dt^2} + RC \frac{dv}{dt} + v = V_p \sin \omega t \tag{3.6}$$

The solution of Eq. (3.6) may now be obtained in exactly the manner considered in Chapter 2. To begin with, the natural response of the circuit is found by solving the homogeneous equation

$$LC \frac{d^2v}{dt^2} + RC \frac{dv}{dt} + v = 0 \tag{3.7}$$

The precise solution of Eq. (3.7) will depend on the particular values of L, C and R. This was just the case which arose in Chapter 2 when examining the over-, under- and critically damped response of a simple LCR circuit to a step function input. Providing $R > 0$ (and it would be impossible to practically construct a circuit of the type shown in Fig. 3.4 for which this is not true) we know that the natural response will have one of the following forms:

$$v = A_1 e^{a_1 t} + A_2 e^{a_2 t} \tag{3.8}$$

or

$$v = A_1 e^{a_1 t} + A_2 t e^{a_1 t} \tag{3.9}$$

or

$$v = A_1 e^{a_1 t} \sin (\omega_0 t + \theta) \tag{3.10}$$

It is not necessary for our present purposes to find which of Eqs. (3.8) to (3.10) applies. What is important, however, is to recall that a_1 and a_2 will be negative for passive circuits, and so the natural response will tend to zero as time tends to infinity.

We may now return to Eq. (3.6).

$$LC \frac{d^2v}{dt^2} + RC \frac{dv}{dt} + v = V_p \sin \omega t \tag{3.6}$$

From the earlier discussion, the particular integral solution to this equation can be expected to be sinusoidal of frequency ω, and having an amplitude change and phase shift with respect to the input $v_{in} = V_p \sin \omega t$. We may therefore suggest that the solution is $v = E \sin(\omega t + \phi)$, and try this in Eq. (3.6).

Noting that

$$\frac{dv}{dt} = E\omega \cos(\omega t + \phi)$$

and

$$\frac{d^2v}{dt^2} = -E\omega^2 \sin(\omega t + \phi)$$

Eq. (3.6) becomes

$$-E\omega^2 LC \sin(\omega t + \phi) + E\omega RC \cos(\omega t + \phi) + E \sin(\omega t + \phi) = V_p \sin \omega t \tag{3.11}$$

The task is to find E and ϕ which satisfy Eq. (3.11), and hence show that the guess solution $v = E \sin(\omega t + \phi)$ is correct. Now Eq. (3.11) holds for all time t, and so we can select particular times in an attempt to find E and ϕ. For example, choosing $t = 0$, Eq. (3.11) becomes

$$-E\omega^2 LC \sin \phi + E\omega RC \cos \phi + E \sin \phi = 0$$

Providing $E \neq 0$, we have

$$(1 - \omega^2 LC) \sin \phi + \omega RC \cos \phi = 0$$

i.e.,

$$\tan \phi = \frac{-\omega RC}{1 - \omega^2 LC} \tag{3.12}$$

Thus

$$\phi = \tan^{-1}\left[\frac{-\omega RC}{1 - \omega^2 LC}\right] \tag{3.13}$$

To find E, one possibility is to examine Eq. (3.11) for a time t such that $\omega t + \phi = 2\pi$, that is $t = (2\pi - \phi)/\omega$. Eq. (3.11) becomes

$$-E\omega^2 LC \sin 2\pi + E\omega RC \cos 2\pi + E \sin 2\pi = V_p \sin(2\pi - \phi)$$

Noting that $\sin(2\pi - \phi) = -\sin \phi$, this last equation gives

$$E\omega RC = -V_p \sin \phi \tag{3.14}$$

With the aid of Eq. (3.12) and Fig. 3.5, we see that

$$\sin \phi = \frac{-\omega RC}{[(1 - \omega^2 LC)^2 + \omega^2 R^2 C^2]^{1/2}}$$

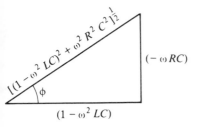

Fig. 3.5 Derivation of cos ϕ and sin ϕ

and so Eq. (3.14) becomes

$$E\omega RC = \frac{V_p \omega RC}{[(1 - \omega^2 LC)^2 + \omega^2 R^2 C^2]^{1/2}}$$

and finally,

$$E = \frac{V_p}{[(1 - \omega^2 LC)^2 + \omega^2 R^2 C^2]^{1/2}} \tag{3.15}$$

The complete response of the circuit shown in Fig. 3.4 when driven by an input voltage $v_{in} = V_p \sin \omega t$ is seen, using Eq. (3.13) and Eq. (3.15), to be

$$v = \left\{ \frac{V_p}{[(1 - \omega^2 LC)^2 + \omega^2 R^2 C^2]^{1/2}} \right\} \sin(\omega t + \phi) + \text{natural response}$$

with

$$\phi = \tan^{-1} \left[\frac{-\omega RC}{1 - \omega^2 LC} \right]$$

We have already seen that as time tends to infinity (which for practical purposes, simply means that time becomes large compared with the time constants of the circuit), the natural response will die to zero. For this reason, this part of the output is often known as the *transient response*. The remaining part of the response, however, will continue to vary sinusoidally for all time, and characterizes the steady, repeating part of the output which is left when the transients have died away. We therefore speak of the *steady-state* response of the circuit as having amplitude

$$\frac{V_p}{[(1 - \omega^2 LC)^2 + \omega^2 R^2 C^2]^{1/2}}$$

and phase

$$\phi = \tan^{-1} \left[\frac{-\omega RC}{1 - \omega^2 LC} \right]$$

with respect to the input, it being implicitly understood that the steady state response is a sinusoid having the same frequency, ω, as the input.

Example

Determine and compare the transient and steady state components of the output v for the circuit shown in Fig. 3.6.

We see here that the input frequency is $\omega = 10^4$ radians/second $\left(\equiv \dfrac{10^4}{2\pi} = 1.59 \text{ kHz} \right)$, and the peak input voltage is $V_p = 2$ volts. Setting $L = 5 \times 10^{-2}$ H, $C = 10^{-7}$ F and $R = 1.5 \times 10^3 \,\Omega$, Eq. (3.6) becomes:

$$5 \times 10^{-9} \frac{d^2v}{dt^2} + 1.5 \times 10^{-4} \frac{dv}{dt} + v = 2 \sin (10^4 t)$$

To find the transient, or natural response, we set $v = Ae^{at}$, and substitute into the homogeneous equation to get

$$5 \times 10^{-9}a^2 + 1.5 \times 10^{-4}a + 1 = 0$$

which yields

$$a_1 = -10^4 \text{ and } a_2 = -2 \times 10^4$$

The transient part of the response is seen to be overdamped, and may be written as

$$v_t = A_1 e^{-10^4 t} + A_2 e^{-2 \times 10^4 t}$$

and the coefficients A_1 and A_2 remain to be found from the initial conditions.

To find the steady state response $E \sin (\omega t + \phi)$ we may simply invoke Eq. (3.13) and Eq. (3.15), which give:

$$\phi = \tan^{-1} \left[\frac{-10^4 \times 1.5 \times 10^3 \times 10^{-7}}{1 - 10^8 \times 5 \times 10^{-2} \times 10^{-7}} \right]$$
$$= -1.25 \text{ radians} \ (\equiv -71.57°)$$

and

$$E = \frac{2}{[(1 - 10^8 \times 5 \times 10^{-2} \times 10^{-7})^2 + 10^8 \times 2.25 \times 10^6 \times 10^{-14}]^{1/2}}$$
$$= 1.26 \text{ volts}$$

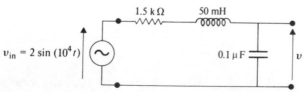

Fig. 3.6 Circuit example

The steady state part of the response is therefore

$$v_{ss} = 1.26 \sin (10^4 t - 1.25)$$

The complete response $v = v_t + v_{ss}$ is

$$v = 1.26 \sin (10^4 t - 1.25) + A_1 e^{-10^4 t} + A_2 e^{-2 \times 10^4 t} \tag{3.16}$$

To find A_1 and A_2, we examine the initial conditions, as discussed in Chapter 2. At time $t = 0$, the input voltage ($2 \sin 10^4 t$) is zero, and so the current i and output voltage v in Fig. 3.6 will be zero. Since for the capacitor $i = 10^{-7} \dfrac{dv}{dt}$, we see that at $t = 0$, $\dfrac{dv}{dt}$ will also be zero. Thus, in Eq. (3.16), at $t = 0$ we have

$$0 = 1.26 \sin (-1.25) + A_1 + A_2$$

which gives

$$A_1 + A_2 = 1.2 \tag{3.17}$$

Differentiating Eq. (3.16) with respect to time, and setting $t = 0$ we also have

$$0 = 1.26 \times 10^4 \cos (-1.25) = -10^4 A_1 - 2 \times 10^4 A_2$$

which gives

$$A_1 + 2A_2 = 0.40 \tag{3.18}$$

From Eq. (3.17) and Eq. (3.18), we finally find $A_1 = 2.0$, $A_2 = -0.8$, and the complete response (Eq. (3.16)) becomes

$$v = 1.26 \sin (10^4 t - 1.25) + 2.0 e^{-10^4 t} - 0.8 e^{-2 \times 10^4 t} \tag{3.19}$$

We may obtain a quantitative assessment of the relative contributions of the transient and steady state parts of the complete response by considering the magnitude of the transient response after one complete cycle of the steady state component from time $t = 0$. The steady state response has a frequency of 1.59 kHz, and so one cycle will have been executed after $\dfrac{1}{(1.59 \times 10^3)} = 6.29 \times 10^{-4}$ s. The transient response component at this time will therefore have magnitude

$$v_t = 2.0 e^{-6.29} - 0.8 e^{-12.58} = 3.73 \times 10^{-3} \text{ volts}$$

The peak steady state voltage is 1.26 volts, and so after only one cycle of the steady state output, the transient response is merely $\dfrac{3.73 \times 10^{-3}}{1.26} \times 100 \simeq$ 0.3% of this peak voltage, and is decreasing exponentially with time. The steady state output voltage is therefore achieved very rapidly, and an oscilloscope trace of the output voltage of the circuit would reveal, for all practical purposes, only the steady state response—a sinusoid with peak voltage 1.26, and a lagging phase shift (since ϕ is negative) of 1.25 radians, that is 71.57°.

In this section we have uncovered, through example, several important properties which apply in general to all linear circuits, when driven by a sinusoidal signal source. In particular we have established the concepts of the transient and steady-state components of the output response, and have seen that the steady state response is sinusoidal in nature, but has an amplitude change and a phase shift with respect to the input signal. This phase shift is said to be leading or lagging according to whether the output is effectively advanced or retarded in time with respect to the input signal. The example chosen was based on the calculation of an output voltage for a sinusoidal input voltage, but any combination of current or voltage as the input or output signal would have yielded the same general principles.

The steady state response analysis conducted in this section required the formulation of the differential equation characterizing the circuit; the substitution of a likely sinusoidal solution to this equation; and finally the determination of the unknowns in the trial solution. This process, if applied in general, would be quite complex for complicated circuits and their associated high order differential equations, and even for the simple circuit considered it is at best tedious. Since the determination of sinusoidal steady state response is a common feature of the engineer's application of circuit theory, it is of interest to consider another approach to the problem.

3.2 VECTOR REPRESENTATION OF SINUSOIDS

If we state the frequency of a sinusoidal signal, the signal is then completely characterized by a knowledge of its peak value or amplitude, (or alternatively its r.m.s. value), and its phase angle measured with respect to some reference. If we take the phase angle to indicate a direction (a point which will shortly become clear), then the amplitude/phase description has all the attributes of a vector, since this may be defined as a quantity having magnitude and direction. Consider a vector **V**, shown in Fig. 3.7. (Bold type will be used for the time being to indicate a vector, but when the reader is conversant with the techniques to be described, it will be shown that this notation may be dropped). The vector **V** is fully described by its length V (often referred to as its *modulus, magnitude* or *amplitude*) and its angle ϕ with respect to the right hand horizontal or *reference* axis. ϕ is also often known as the argument of **V**. Mathematically we may write

$$\mathbf{V} = V\underline{/\phi}$$

to express the fact that **V** is a vector of magnitude V and angle ϕ to the

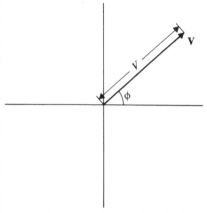

Fig. 3.7 A vector represented on the Argand diagram

reference axis. This notation is known as the *polar form* of the vector **V**. Also the notations $V = |\mathbf{V}|$, $\phi = \arg \mathbf{V}$ are generally used to show that $|\mathbf{V}|$ is the magnitude of **V**, and ϕ is the argument of **V**, that is the angle associated with it.

The set of axes, together with the vector **V**, constitute an *Argand Diagram*, which is a means of depicting vectors graphically. We may now consider the representation of another vector on the Argand Diagram. Consider a vector $\mathbf{V}_1 = V \big/\!\!\underline{\phi + \dfrac{\pi}{2}}$. This vector has the same magnitude as **V**, but has an angle which is $\dfrac{\pi}{2}$ radians (90°) greater than **V**. Taking an anticlockwise direction as corresponding to increasing angle, we may represent $\mathbf{V}_1$ as shown in Fig. 3.8.

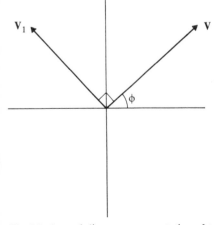

Fig. 3.8 Argand diagram representation of two vectors

At this point, we shall introduce ·a very important concept. Since V_1 is identical to V, with the exception that its argument is 90° greater, we shall write

$$V_1 = jV$$

where j is the 90° *phase operator.* In other words, $V_1 = jV$ simply means that V_1 is obtained from V by rotating V by 90° in an anticlockwise direction. If we use the notation that j^2V implies applying the 90° phase operator twice, and j^3V three times, we may depict the resulting vectors as shown in Fig. 3.9(a). It is important to appreciate that j^2 does not imply the squaring of some algebraic quantity j, any more than $\dfrac{d^2}{dt^2}$ implies the

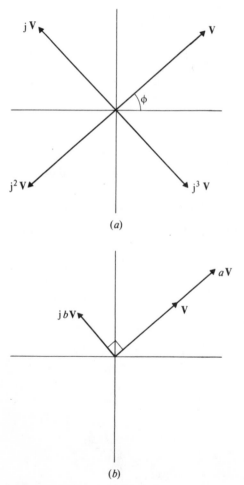

(a)

(b)

Fig. 3.9 (a) 90° phase shifting operation on a vector (b) phase and scalar operation on a vector

squaring of the differential operator $\dfrac{d}{dt}$, but that it merely means that the vector j^2V is obtained from V by applying two 90° phase operations.

We see from Fig. 3.9 that $j^2V = -V$, the negative sign indicating that the vector is drawn in a direction opposite to V. This identity is of frequent use in the manipulation of vectors. The reader may be tempted to further develop this identity by cancelling V on both sides to give $j^2 = -1$, and then suggest that $j = \sqrt{-1}$, a purely imaginary number. Such a step is totally erroneous in the present context, since we have seen that we are using j as an *operator*, and $\sqrt{-1}$ has no relevance to this use. However, there is some connection between our use of j as a 90° phase operator, and its interpretation as an imaginary number, and we shall presently see this connection encroaching on the terminology which is used with the Argand Diagram.

Using $j^2V = -V$, it will be seen that $j^3V = -jV$. This indicates that j^3V, which is the vector V rotated by $\dfrac{3\pi}{2}$ radians or 270°, may also be obtained by operating on V by $-j$. In other words, $-j$ is seen to rotate the vector V by $\dfrac{-\pi}{2}$ radians, or $-90°$, this being a rotation in the clockwise sense on the Argand Diagram.

The vector V may also be changed in magnitude using an obvious notation. Thus $V_1 = aV$ is a vector whose magnitude is $a|V|$, and angle identical to V, while $V_1 = jbV$ alters the magnitude by the factor b, and rotates V through 90° to give V_1. This is summarized in Fig. 3.9(b).

An alternative notation for vectors is obtained by resolving the vector into the *orthogonal* components (that is at right angles to each other) as shown in Fig. 3.10.

If we denote **1** as a vector of unit magnitude, parallel to the reference axis, then using the arrowhead to tail convention for vectors (sometimes known as the parallelogram rule), we may write

$$V = a\mathbf{1} + jb\mathbf{1} \qquad (3.20)$$

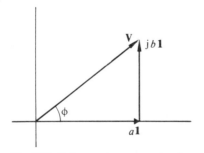

Fig. 3.10 Orthogonal components of a vector

or

$$\mathbf{V} = (a + jb) \tag{3.21}$$

it being implicitly understood in Eq. (3.21) that the quantity $(a + jb)$ is an operator on the unit vector **1**. The notation stated in Eq. (3.21) may be simply interpreted as: to find vector **V**, move from the origin a units parallel to the horizontal axis, followed by b units parallel to the vertical axis in the Argand Diagram. The vector **V** is then drawn from the origin and directed towards the point which has been arrived at in this way.

Because of the association of j with the imaginary number $\sqrt{-1}$, it has become conventional to refer to a (or strictly $a\mathbf{1}$) as the *real part* of the vector $\mathbf{V} = (a + jb)$, and to b (strictly $b\mathbf{1}$) as the *imaginary* part of **V**. For the same reason, the horizontal and vertical axes in the Argand Diagram are referred to as the real and imaginary axes respectively.

The operator $(a + jb)$, which is known as a complex number, expresses the vector **V** in its *rectangular form*. Another form is obtained by noting that $|\mathbf{V}| = (a^2 + b^2)^{1/2}$, and that $a = |\mathbf{V}| \cos \phi$, $b = |\mathbf{V}| \sin \phi$ from which

$$\mathbf{V} = |\mathbf{V}| (\cos \phi + j \sin \phi)\mathbf{1}$$

or

$$\mathbf{V} = |\mathbf{V}| (\cos \phi + j \sin \phi) \tag{3.22}$$

with $\phi = \tan^{-1}\left(\dfrac{b}{a}\right)$.

Eq. (3.22) is directly equivalent to Eq. (3.21), but represents the so-called *trignometric form* of the vector **V**. Now $\cos \phi$ may be represented by its power series expansion, giving

$$\cos \phi \mathbf{1} = \left[1 - \frac{\phi^2}{2!} + \frac{\phi^4}{4!} - \frac{\phi^6}{6!} + \cdots \right]\mathbf{1}$$

which may be written as

$$\cos \phi \mathbf{1} = \left[1 + \frac{(j\phi)^2}{2!} + \frac{(j\phi)^4}{4!} + \frac{(j\phi)^6}{6!} + \cdots \right]\mathbf{1}$$

since $j^2\mathbf{1} = -\mathbf{1}$.

Similarly,

$$j \sin \phi \mathbf{1} = j\left[\phi - \frac{\phi^3}{3!} + \frac{\phi^5}{5!} - \frac{\phi^7}{7!} + \cdots \right]\mathbf{1}$$

$$= \left[(j\phi) + \frac{(j\phi)^3}{3!} + \frac{(j\phi)^5}{5!} + \frac{(j\phi)^7}{7!} + \cdots \right]\mathbf{1}$$

The expression $(\cos \phi + j \sin \phi)\mathbf{1}$ may therefore be written as

$$\left[1 + (j\phi) + \frac{(j\phi)^2}{2!} + \frac{(j\phi)^3}{3!} + \frac{(j\phi)^4}{4!} + \cdots \right]\mathbf{1}$$

or $(\cos \phi + j \sin \phi)\mathbf{1} = e^{j\phi}\mathbf{1}$ where we have recognized the power series expansion of $e^{j\phi}$ in the above expression. The identity

$$e^{j\phi} = \cos \phi + j \sin \phi$$

is known as the *Euler identity*, and leads to an alternative *exponential form* of the vector **V**, namely

$$\mathbf{V} = |\mathbf{V}|e^{j\phi}\mathbf{1}$$

or

$$\mathbf{V} = |\mathbf{V}|e^{j\phi} \tag{3.23}$$

To summarize, we have introduced four alternative ways of expressing the vector **V**, namely:

$$\mathbf{V} = |\mathbf{V}|\underline{/\phi} \qquad \text{(Polar form)}$$
$$\mathbf{V} = a + jb \qquad \text{(Rectangular form)}$$
$$\mathbf{V} = |\mathbf{V}|(\cos \phi + j \sin \phi) \quad \text{(Trignometric form)}$$
$$\mathbf{V} = |\mathbf{V}|e^{j\phi} \qquad \text{(Exponential form)}$$

Remember that the unit vector **1** is implicitly understood to be associated with the right hand sides of all but the first of the above expressions. Since the various forms are merely alternative ways of describing the same vector, it is clearly possible to interchange between them, as the following example shows.

Example

Find alternative forms for vectors (i) $\mathbf{V} = 6.2\underline{/\frac{\pi}{6}}$ radians, (ii) $\mathbf{V} = 2 + j3$

(i) Here we have $|\mathbf{V}| = 6.2$, $\phi = \frac{\pi}{6}$

We may immediately write the exponential form:

$$\mathbf{V} = 6.2e^{j\pi/6}$$

which leads to the trignometric form

$$\mathbf{V} = 6.2\left(\cos \frac{\pi}{6} + j \sin \frac{\pi}{6}\right)$$

Evaluating the cosine and the sine,

$$\mathbf{V} = 6.2(0.866 + j0.5)$$

i.e.,

$$\mathbf{V} = 5.639 + j3.1$$

The vector **V** therefore has a real component of magnitude 5.369, and an imaginary component with magnitude 3.1.

(ii) In this case, the vector is expressed in rectangular form, $V = 2 + j3$. The magnitude of the vector is $|V| = (2^2 + 3^2)^{1/2} = 3.606$; and its argument is $\phi = \tan^{-1}\left(\frac{3}{2}\right) = 0.983$ radians. Thus, the polar form is $V = 3.606\underline{/0.983}$, the exponential form is $3.606e^{j0.983}$, and finally, the trignometric form is $V = 3.606 (\cos (0.963) + j \sin (0.963))$.

The alternative vector notations are useful in the manipulation of vectors. For example, consider the vectors $V_1 = a_1 + jb_1$ and $V_2 = a_2 + jb_2$. Then

$$V_1 + V_2 = a_1 + jb_1 + a_2 + jb_2 = (a_1 + a_1) + j(b_1 + b_2)$$

This shows that the real and imaginary parts of the composite vector $V_1 + V_2$ are obtained by adding the real and imaginary parts, respectively, of the constituent vectors. This is shown pictorially in Fig. 3.11.

The rectangular form is seen to be particularly useful for the addition of vectors. When adding vectors represented in any other form, they may be converted to rectangular form, added, and then the result may be reconverted as desired. Subtraction of vectors is carried out in the same manner.

The rectangular notation $V = a + jb$ was obtained from the application of the complex operator $(a + jb)$ on the unit vector 1. A vector may also be defined through a similar operation on any other vector. As an example, let

$$V_1 = (c + jd)V$$

The rectangular form of V_1 may be found by writing

$$V_1 = (c + jd)(a + jb)1$$

where the unit vector has been included to clarify the manipulation. Expanding the right hand side,

$$V_1 = (ac + jad + jbc + j^2bd)1$$

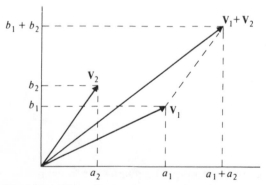

Fig. 3.11 Addition of vectors

Noting that $j^2 bd1 = - bd1$, the expression becomes

$$V_1 = [(ac - bd) + j(ad + bc)]1$$

The rectangular form of the resulting vector is therefore $V_1 = (ac - bd) + j(ad + bc)$. This process is simplified if the vector V is written in exponential form, and the Euler identity is used for the complex operator $(c + jd)$. If $V = |V|e^{j\phi}$, and $(c + jd) = re^{j\theta}$, where $r = (c^2 + d^2)^{1/2}$ and $\theta = \tan^{-1}\left(\dfrac{d}{c}\right)$, then

$$V_1 = re^{j\theta}|V|e^{j\phi}1 = (r|V|)e^{j(\phi + \theta)}1$$

and so V_1 has the exponential form $V_1 = (r|V|)e^{j(\phi + \theta)}$.

We may now consider the inverse problem. Suppose $V_1 = (c + jd)V = (e + jf)$, and the vector V is to be found. First the vector V_1 is operated upon by $(c - jd)$ which is the *complex conjugate* of $(c + jd)$. This gives

$$(c - jd)(c + jd)V = (c - jd)(e + jf)1$$

i.e.,

$$(c^2 + d^2)V = [(ce + df) + j(cf - ed)]1$$

Now $(c^2 + d^2)$ is a real number, and so dividing through,

$$V = \left[\frac{(ce + df)}{(c^2 + d^2)} + j\frac{(cf - ed)}{(c^2 + d^2)}\right]1$$

which gives the rectangular form for V. Equivalently, but less rigorously, this last manipulation may be obtained in the following manner:

$$V = \frac{(e + jf)}{(c + jd)} = \frac{(c - jd)(e + jf)}{(c - jd)(c + jd)} = \left[\frac{(ce + df)}{(c^2 + d^2)} + j\frac{(cf - ed)}{(c^2 + d^2)}\right]$$

The process of reducing the quotient of two operators in rectangular form is known as *rationalisation*. Again, the exponential form provides some simplification. If $V_1 = |V_1|e^{j\phi}$ and using $(c + jd) = re^{j\theta}$ as before, then $V_1 = re^{j\theta}V$, and so

$$re^{j\theta}V = |V_1|e^{j\phi}1$$

$$\therefore \qquad V = \frac{|V_1|}{r}e^{j(\phi - \theta)}1$$

giving the exponential form of V.

These last two manipulations are akin to arithmetic multiplication and division, and the exponential forms are most appropriate in such cases.

Example

Given $V_1 = j3$, $V_2 = 4e^{j\pi/6}$, find (i) $V_3 = V_1 + V_2$, (ii) $V_4 = (3 + j4)V_2$, (iii) V_5 where $V_1 = (2 - j1)V_5$.

(i)
$$V_3 = j3 + 4e^{j\pi/6} = (0 + j3) + 4\left(\cos\frac{\pi}{6} + j\sin\frac{\pi}{6}\right)$$
$$= (0 + 3.46) + j(3 + 2) = 3.46 + j5$$

Now $|V_3| = (3.46^2 + 5^2)^{1/2} = 6.08$, and $\arg(V_3) = \tan^{-1}\left(\frac{5}{3.46}\right) = 0.965$ radians. Equivalently, therefore, $V_3 = 6.08\underline{/0.965}$ or $V_3 = 6.08e^{j0.965}$.

(ii) Using the Euler identity, $(3 + j4) = (3^2 + 4^2)^{1/2}e^{j\theta}$, $\theta = \tan^{-1}\left(\frac{4}{3}\right)$ i.e.,

$$3 + j4 = 5e^{j0.927}$$

$\therefore$
$$V_4 = 5e^{j0.927}4e^{j\pi/6} = 20e^{j1.451}$$

Alternatively, in rectangular form,

$$V_4 = 20(\cos 1.451 + j\sin 1.451) = 2.392 + j19.856$$

(iii)
$$V_5 = \frac{j3}{2 - j1} = \frac{(2 + j1)j3}{(2^2 + 1^2)} = \frac{-3}{5} + j\frac{6}{5} = -0.6 + j1.2$$

We are now in a position to consider how vectors might assist in the representation of time domain voltages and currents. For example, consider the time domain voltage $v_1 = V_1 \cos \omega t$. From the preceding discussion, we see that we may represent this voltage by the real axis projection of a vector $V_1 = V_1\underline{/\omega t}$ or equivalently $V_1 = V_1e^{j\omega t}$, since this projection is $V_1 \cos \omega t$, as required. This is shown in Fig. 3.12.

Since the phase angle ωt, (which is the argument of V_1), is increasing with time, we see that the vector $V_1 = V_1e^{j\omega t}$ is in fact spinning around the origin of the Argand diagram with angular frequency ω rad/s. To draw Fig. 3.12, we therefore have to freeze the diagram at some point in time.

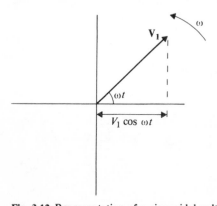

Fig. 3.12 Representation of a sinusoidal voltage by a vector

With this representation, we merely have to write

$$v_1 = Re[\mathbf{V}_1]$$

in order to express the fact that $v_1 = V_1 \cos \omega t$ is the *real* axis projection of the vector $\mathbf{V}_1$.

We may now introduce a second time domain voltage $v_2 = V_2 \cos (\omega t + \phi)$. In just the same way, this may be represented as the real axis projection of a vector $\mathbf{V}_2 = V_2 e^{j(\omega t + \phi)}$, i.e., $v_2 = Re[\mathbf{V}_2]$. The situation is shown in Fig. 3.13.

$\mathbf{V}_2$ and $\mathbf{V}_1$ are both rotating at angular frequency ω, but maintain a constant phase shift ϕ between each other as they rotate, $\mathbf{V}_2$ leading $\mathbf{V}_1$ by ϕ radians. Also shown in Fig. 3.13 is a vector $\mathbf{V}_3$ which is lagging $\mathbf{V}_1$ by $\dfrac{\pi}{2}$ radians. Thus $\mathbf{V}_3 = |\mathbf{V}_3| e^{j(\omega t - \pi/2)}$. To find what time domain signal this vector represents, we simply write

$$v_3 = Re[\mathbf{V}_3] = Re\left[|\mathbf{V}_3| \left\{ \cos \left(\omega t - \frac{\pi}{2} \right) + j \sin \left(\omega t - \frac{\pi}{2} \right) \right\} \right]$$

$$= |\mathbf{V}_3| \cos \left(\omega t - \frac{\pi}{2} \right)$$

i.e.,

$$v_3 = |\mathbf{V}_3| \sin \omega t$$

In other words, the phase relationship between $\mathbf{V}_1$ and $\mathbf{V}_3$ is such that with $\mathbf{V}_1$ representing (through its real axis projection) a voltage varying as $\cos \omega t$, $\mathbf{V}_3$ represents a voltage varying as $\sin \omega t$. We see that $\mathbf{V}_3$ lags $\mathbf{V}_1$ by $\dfrac{\pi}{2}$ radians, that is, 90°.

Given any set of time domain sinusoidal voltages or currents of the same frequency ω, we may therefore represent them as vectors on an Argand

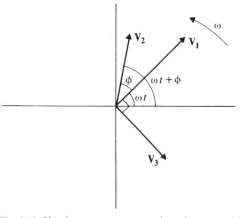

Fig. 3.13 Simultaneous representation of several sinusoidal voltages on the Argand diagram

diagram, providing one vector (conventionally chosen as representing cos ωt) is used as a reference. All the vectors will be rotating with angular frequency ω rad/s but will bear constant phase relationships with each other. Some simplification of the notation results if we stop the vectors spinning in some way. Let us take the example of the Argand diagram shown in Fig. 3.14(a). Here the vectors V_1, I_1 and V_2 represent their respective time domain signals through their real axis projections $v_1 =$

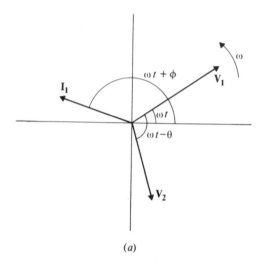

(a)

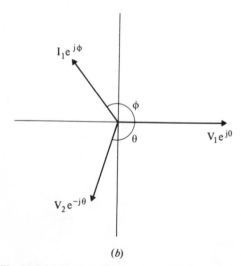

(b)

Fig. 3.14 (a) Vector, (b) phasor representation of sinusoidal signals

$V_1 \cos \omega t$, $i_1 = I_1 \cos (\omega t + \phi)$ and $v_2 = V_2 \cos (\omega t - \theta)$. Using the exponential notation, we may write

$$\left. \begin{aligned} \mathbf{V}_1 &= V_1 e^{j\omega t} = V_1 e^{j0} e^{j\omega t} \\ \mathbf{I}_1 &= I_1 e^{j(\omega t + \phi)} = I_1 e^{j\phi} e^{j\omega t} \\ \mathbf{V}_2 &= V_2 e^{j(\omega t - \theta)} = V_2 e^{-j\theta} e^{j\omega t} \end{aligned} \right\} \tag{3.24}$$

We see that as a result of all the time domain signals being at the same frequency, each of the vectors in Eq. (3.24) may be written with a common term $e^{j\omega t}$ on the right hand side. If we ignore this term, the resulting expressions: $V_1 e^{j0}$, $I_1 e^{j\phi}$, $V_2 e^{-j\theta}$ are still vectors, and contain all the amplitude and phase information which we seek. These vectors are drawn in Fig. 3.14(b) and, of course, they are static. Because these vectors ignore the variation of their arguments with time, but still express the phase relationships with each other, they are known as *phase vectors*, a term which is abbreviated to *phasors*. Given a phasor, for example $I_2 e^{j\psi}$, we may find its time domain representation as follows. First of all we find the associated vector, which is simply $I_2 e^{j\psi} \cdot e^{j\omega t} = I_2 e^{j(\omega t + \psi)}$. Now we find the real axis projection giving

$$i_2 = Re[I_2 e^{j(\omega t + \psi)}] = I_2 \cos (\omega t + \psi)$$

To summarize:

$$\underset{\text{phasor}}{I_2 e^{j\psi}} \rightarrow \underset{\text{vector}}{I_2 e^{j\psi} \cdot e^{j\omega t} = I_2 e^{j(\omega t + \psi)}} \rightarrow \underset{\text{real axis projection}}{i_2 = Re[I_2 e^{j(\omega t + \psi)}]} \underset{\text{time domain signal}}{= I_2 \cos (\omega t + \psi)}$$

In other words, providing that we understand the intermediate steps, we may write the equivalence as

$$\underset{\text{phasor}}{I_2 e^{j\psi}} \rightarrow \underset{\text{time domain signal}}{i_2 = I_2 \cos (\omega t + \psi)} \tag{3.25}$$

This last expression (Eq. (3.25)) summarizes the equivalence between the *frequency domain phasor* $I_2 e^{j\psi}$, and the *time domain signal* $i_2 = I_2 \cos (\omega t + \psi)$.

Example

Find the 50 Hz sinusoidal time domain signal corresponding to the phasor $3 + j4$ volts.

Here the phasor has been expressed in rectangular form. First we convert this to exponential form. The magnitude of the phasor is given by $(3^2 + 4^2)^{1/2} = 5$ volts, while its argument is $\tan^{-1}\left(\dfrac{4}{3}\right) = 0.927$ radians ($\equiv 53.13°$). The exponential form of the phasor is therefore $5e^{j0.927}$. The vector associated with this phasor is $5e^{j0.927} \cdot e^{j100\pi t}$, that is, $5e^{j(100\pi t + 0.927)}$.

Finally, the time domain signal is seen to be $5 \cos (100\pi t + 0.927)$ volts. Clearly, we could have arrived at this result more directly using Eq. (3.25).

Example

Find the phasor representation of the current $i = 4 \sin (37t + 1.2)$.

Note that the frequency of this sinusoid (37 radians/second) is of no real concern to us in finding the phasor equivalent. However, since we have been using $\cos \omega t$ as our reference for the phasor representation, we must first write

$$i = 4 \sin (37t + 1.2) = 4 \cos \left(37t + 1.2 - \frac{\pi}{2}\right)$$

Inserting a value for π, we obtain

$$i = 4 \cos (37t - 0.371)$$

Using Eq. (3.25), we immediately obtain the phasor representation of i as $4e^{-j0.371}$. This is shown in Fig. 3.15 where it is seen that the phasor lags the reference phasor (assumed lying on the real axis) by 0.371 radians ($= 21.25°$).

Having obtained the phasor, any of the other vector forms may be derived from it.

We shall now consider the phasor representation of sinusoidal signals in relation to the basic two terminal circuit components of Resistance, Capacitance, and Inductance. To accomplish this, we shall apply a voltage $v = V \cos \omega t$ to each of the components in turn, and derive the phasor representation of the current which results.

(i) *Resistance*

Ohm's Law gives the defining relationship for a resistor:

$$i = \frac{v}{R}$$

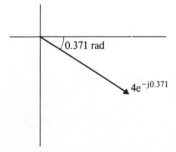

Fig. 3.15 Phasor representation of $i = 4 \sin (37t + 1.2)$

With $v = V \cos \omega t$, we have $i = \dfrac{V}{R} \cos \omega t$.

If the time domain voltage is represented by the phasor $\mathbf{V}$, then the current phasor $\mathbf{I}$ associated with it is related according to

$$\mathbf{I} = \frac{1}{R}\mathbf{V} \tag{3.26}$$

In other words, $\mathbf{I}$ and $\mathbf{V}$ are in phase (since there is no phase shift between voltage and current in a resistor), and $\mathbf{I}$ is obtained from $\mathbf{V}$ by the scalar (that is, changing the scale) operation of dividing by the resistance R. The two phasors are shown in Fig. 3.16.

Equivalently, if a current were applied to the resistor, then $\mathbf{V} = R\mathbf{I}$. We see that Ohm's Law is obeyed between the voltage and current phasors in the frequency domain. The operator R (which is in this case a scalar operator) is known as the *impedance* of the resistor, and it is numerically equal to its resistance. The quantity $\dfrac{1}{R}$ is the *admittance* of the component and is given by the conductance of the resistor. The resistance in ohms relates the magnitudes of the voltage and current vectors, i.e., $R = |\mathbf{V}|/|\mathbf{I}|$. It is tempting to say that impedance is the ratio of voltage to current phasors $\dfrac{\mathbf{V}}{\mathbf{I}}$, and admittance is given by the inverse ratio $\dfrac{\mathbf{I}}{\mathbf{V}}$. Indeed, although this notation is not strictly valid (since the quotient of two phasors is undefined), it is in frequent use.

(ii) *Capacitance*

For a capacitor the time domain defining relationship is $i = C\dfrac{dv}{dt}$. With

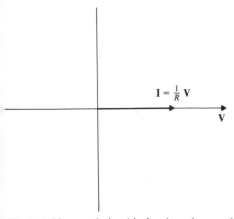

$$\mathbf{I} = \tfrac{1}{R}\mathbf{V}$$

Fig. 3.16 Phasor relationship for the voltage and current in a resistor

$v = V \cos \omega t$, $i = -\omega C V \sin \omega t$

i.e.,

$$i = \omega C V \cos\left(\omega t + \frac{\pi}{2}\right) \tag{3.27}$$

In terms of the phasor representations,

$$\mathbf{I} = j\omega C \mathbf{V} \tag{3.28}$$

Eq. (3.28) shows that the current phasor is obtained from the voltage phasor by changing its scale by ωC, and shifting the phase by $\frac{\pi}{2}$ radians. The 'j' operation is to take account of the phase shift evident in Eq. (3.27). The two phasors are shown in Fig. 3.17.

Fig. 3.17 shows diagrammatically what is suggested by Eq. (3.28), namely that for a capacitor, the current leads the voltage by $\frac{\pi}{2}$ radians, that is 90°.

From Eq. (3.28) we have

$$\mathbf{V} = \frac{1}{j\omega C}\mathbf{I} = \frac{-j}{\omega C}\,I \tag{3.29}$$

The quantity $\frac{1}{j\omega C}$ or equivalently $\frac{-j}{\omega C}$ is the impedance of the capacitor, while the quantity $\frac{-1}{\omega C}$ is known as its *reactance*. The admittance of the capacitor on the other hand is $j\omega C$, the quantity ωC being known as its *susceptance*.

In terms of the magnitudes of the voltage and current phasors, $\dfrac{|\mathbf{V}|}{|\mathbf{I}|} = \dfrac{1}{\omega C}$. This shows that under sinusoidal excitation the capacitor tends to an open

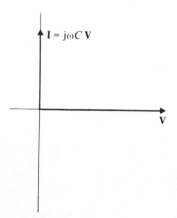

Fig. 3.17 Phasor relationship for the voltage and current in a capacitor

circuit at very low frequencies, and a short circuit at very high frequencies, since the *magnitude of the impedance*, $\frac{1}{\omega C}$, is inversely proportional to frequency.

The most important point to be noted from Eq. (3.28) and Eq. (3.29) is that the voltage and current phasors are related algebraically. This is our first glimpse of the whole raison d'être of the phasor approach—an approach which transforms the time domain differential relationships into frequency domain algebraic relationships.

(iii) *Inductance*

For an inductor, the current is obtained from the integral relationship

$$i = \frac{1}{L} \int_0^t v \cdot \mathrm{d}t + i(0)$$

The initial current $i(0)$ will not contribute to the steady state sinusoidal response in which we are interested, so disregarding this, and substituting $v = V \cos \omega t$, we obtain

$$i = \frac{V}{\omega L} \sin \omega t = \frac{V}{\omega L} \cos \left(\omega t - \frac{\pi}{2} \right) \tag{3.30}$$

The phasor relationship is therefore

$$\mathbf{I} = \frac{-\mathrm{j}}{\omega L} \mathbf{V} \tag{3.31}$$

from which it is seen that the current lags the voltage in an inductor by 90°. The Argand diagram for the inductor phasors is shown in Fig. 3.18.

Alternatively, Eq. (3.31) may be written as

$$\mathbf{V} = \mathrm{j}\omega L \mathbf{I}$$

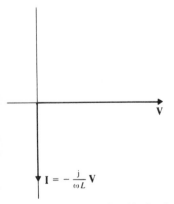

Fig. 3.18 Phasor relationship for the voltage and current in an inductor

The inductor also clearly exhibits an algebraic relationship between its voltage and current phasors. In this case the inductor has impedance $j\omega L$ and admittance $\dfrac{-j}{\omega L}$; while the reactance of the inductor is ωL, and its susceptance is $\dfrac{-1}{\omega L}$.

We have seen that the three basic circuit components of Resistance, Capacitance, and Inductance all exhibit a relationship of the form $\mathbf{V} = Z\mathbf{I}$ between the voltage and current phasors in the frequency domain. The general relationship is clearly similar to Ohm's Law for resistors, and in fact the impedance Z is usually measured in ohms. Similarly in the inverse relationship $\mathbf{I} = Y\mathbf{V}$ the admittance Y is measured in siemens. It was seen earlier in this section that the addition of time domain sinusoids is equivalent to the summation of their frequency domain phasor counterparts; in other words, Kirchhoff's Laws also apply to phasors. With this information, the whole motivation for the phasor approach should now be clear, since any sinusoidal response circuit analysis problem may be solved by the application of algebraic rather than differential equation techniques.

3.3   ANALYSIS USING PHASORS

With the tools which have been developed in section 3.2, it is now possible to consider further the steady state frequency domain analysis of circuits.

In the circuit shown in Fig. 3.19, the same phasor voltage $\mathbf{V} = |\mathbf{V}|\underline{/0}$ is applied to the resistor R and capacitor C in parallel. With $\mathbf{I}_R$ and $\mathbf{I}_C$ as the (phasor) currents associated with R and C respectively, we have:

$$\mathbf{I}_R = \frac{1}{R}\mathbf{V} \qquad \mathbf{I}_C = j\omega C\mathbf{V}$$

Using Kirchhoff's Current Law,

$$\mathbf{I} = \mathbf{I}_R + \mathbf{I}_C$$

where $\mathbf{I}$ is the total current.

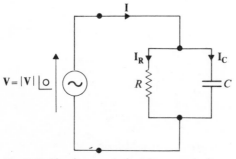

Fig. 3.19 Circuit example for phasor analysis

Thus

$$I = \frac{1}{R}V + j\omega CV \tag{3.32}$$

e.,

$$I = \left(\frac{1}{R} + j\omega C\right)V \tag{3.33}$$

The admittance $\left(\frac{1}{R} + j\omega C\right)$ has real (or *conductive*) part $\frac{1}{R}$, and imaginary (or *susceptive*) part ωC. The Argand diagram for Eq. (3.32) is shown in Fig. 3.20.

Using the Euler identity for the admittance of the circuit, Eq. (3.33) may be written as

$$I = \left(\frac{1}{R^2} + (\omega C)^2\right)^{1/2} e^{j\phi}V$$

where

$$\phi = \tan^{-1}\left(\frac{\omega C}{1/R}\right) = \tan^{-1}(\omega CR) \tag{3.34}$$

and so

$$\frac{|I|}{|V|} = \left(\frac{1}{R^2} + (\omega C)^2\right)^{1/2} \tag{3.35}$$

Eq. (3.34) and Eq. (3.35) may be confirmed from Fig. 3.20.

Let us be clear what has been done in following through Eq. (3.32) to Eq. 3.35). Using the phasor representation of time domain sinusoids we have found the amplitude and phase relationships which the steady state sinusoidal current in the circuit of Fig. 3.19 bear to the sinusoidal input voltage, which has been assumed to be the reference. It is common practice to make the input voltage or current of a circuit have reference phase (i.e. $\underline{/0}$). However, since we are usually only interested in the amplitude and phase of circuit voltages and currents with respect to the

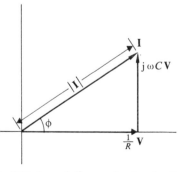

g. 3.20 Argand diagram for the circuit of Fig. 3.19

input, any other input phase could have been chosen without affecting relative results. This is because a shift in the input phase will lead to the same phase shift in all circuit currents and voltages.

As a further point, it will be noted that we have taken quantities such as $|V|$, $|I|$ to be the peak values of the sinusoidal signals which the phasors V and I represent. For example, Eq. (3.35) permits the peak value of current $|I|$ to be found from the peak voltage $|V|$ multiplied by the modulus of the admittance. Now r.m.s. values of both voltage and current sinusoids are found by dividing their peak values by $\sqrt{2}$, and therefore the left hand side of Eq. (3.35) may also be interpreted as the ratio of r.m.s. values. We shall return to this point in Chapter 7 when discussing a.c. power.

To further establish the simplicity of the phasor technique, we may consider again the circuit of Fig. 3.19, but with a current source as input as shown in Fig. 3.21.

Using Eq. (3.33) directly, we have

$$V = \frac{1}{\dfrac{1}{R} + j\omega C}\, I = \frac{R}{1 + j\omega CR}\, I \qquad (3.36)$$

Rationalizing the impedance

$$V = \frac{R(1 - j\omega CR)}{1 + (\omega CR)^2}\, I = \left[\frac{R}{1 + (\omega CR)^2} - \frac{j\omega CR^2}{1 + (\omega CR)^2}\right] I \qquad (3.37)$$

The modulus and phase angle, θ, of V with respect to I may now be found from Eq. (3.37), or more directly from Eq. (3.36):

$$\frac{|V|}{|I|} = \frac{R}{[1 + (\omega CR)^2]^{1/2}}$$

$$\theta = \tan^{-1}\left(\frac{0}{R}\right) - \tan^{-1}\frac{\omega CR}{1}$$

$$= -\tan^{-1}\omega CR$$

Inspection reveals that the ratio of modulii and the phase are the inverse and negative of Eq. (3.35) and Eq. (3.34) respectively. We see

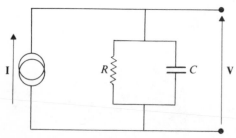

Fig. 3.21 Circuit example with current source input

therefore the importance of the concepts of impedance and (its inverse) admittance. The impedance allows us to calculate the voltage across the circuit which it describes (in both magnitude and phase) given the current, and vice versa for admittance. The reader will observe also that the last example was executed without stating that the input current had reference phase ($\underline{/0}$)—this was implicitly understood and is a common convention. Further, the modulus and phase relationships were determined without recourse to the Argand diagram. This is generally the case, since providing one keeps in one's mind's eye a picture of the diagram, it is rarely that one needs to draw it to perform a circuit analysis.

With the rules, tools and conventions of the phasor approach to the calculation of steady state sinusoidal response at our disposal, we may now return to the circuit of Fig. 3.4, whose analysis in the time domain was discussed in section 3.1. The circuit is redrawn in Fig. 3.22. Noting that the resistor, inductor, and capacitor have impedances R, $j\omega L$ and $\dfrac{1}{j\omega C}$ respectively, and that these quantities algebraically relate the voltage and current phasors associated with each component, we may treat this circuit as a potential divider, and write

$$V = \frac{\dfrac{1}{j\omega C}}{R + j\omega L + \dfrac{1}{j\omega C}} V_{in}$$

or

$$V = \frac{1}{1 + j^2\omega^2 LC + j\omega CR} V_{in} = \frac{1}{(1 - \omega^2 LC) + j\omega CR} V_{in} \qquad (3.38)$$

The operator in Eq. (3.38) is known as the *voltage transfer function* of the circuit, and relates the specified input and output voltages. From Eq. (3.38)

$$\frac{|V|}{|V_{in}|} = \frac{1}{[(1 - \omega^2 LC)^{1/2} + \omega^2 C^2 R^2]^{1/2}}, \quad \phi = -\tan^{-1}\left(\frac{\omega CR}{1 - \omega^2 LC}\right) \qquad (3.39)$$

where ϕ is the phase shift between V and V_{in}. With $|V| = E$, $|V_{in}| = V_p$, these results correspond with Eq. (3.15) and Eq. (3.13) respectively, and were obtained much more directly.

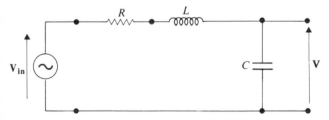

Fig. 3.22 Circuit example

Example

For the circuit of Fig. 3.23(a), find (i) the input impedance Z_{in} which relates V_1 and I_1, (ii) the current transfer function relating I_2 and I_1 both for an input current sinusoid of frequency 1 MHz.

In following through this example, we shall adopt one further convention and drop the use of bold type for phasors. It is difficult to use bold characters in written work, and the use of other similar vector notations can be tedious. Expressing frequency domain phasors by ordinary upper case letters (I_1, V_1 etc) and time domain signals by lower case letters (i_1, v_1 etc.) is usually enough to remind one of the nature of the quantities with which we are dealing.

We begin the analysis of the circuit of Fig. 3.23(a) by redrawing it and appending the impedance of the capacitor and inductor calculated at the frequency $\omega = 2\pi \times 10^6$ rad/sec. For the capacitor, the impedance is

$$\frac{1}{j2\pi \times 10^6 \times 10^{-9}} = -j159.2 \ \Omega$$

and for the inductor it is

$$j2\pi \times 10^6 \times 10^{-3} = j6.28 \text{ k}\Omega$$

(i) The input impedance may be written down by inspection of Fig. 3.23(b):

$$Z_{in} = -j159.2 + \frac{(j6.28 \times 10^3) \times (4.7 \times 10^3)}{(j6.28 \times 10^3) + (4.7 \times 10^3)} \ \Omega$$

$$= -j159.2 + \frac{j29.52 \times 10^3}{4.7 + j6.28} \ \Omega$$

Rationalizing the quotient

$$Z_{in} = -j159.2 + \frac{j29.52 \times 10^3 (4.7 - j6.28)}{(4.7)^2 + (6.28)^2} \ \Omega$$

$$= -j159.2 + j2.255 \times 10^3 + 3.013 \times 10^3 \ \Omega$$

$$= 3.01 \times 10^3 + j2.1 \times 10^3 \ \Omega$$

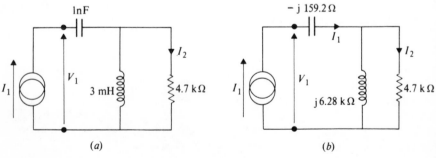

(a)   (b)

Fig. 3.23 Circuit example

Thus

$$|Z_{in}| = \frac{|V_1|}{|I_1|} = \sqrt{(3.01 \times 10^3)^2 + (2.1 \times 10^3)^2} = 3.67 \text{ k}\Omega$$

$$\arg Z_{in} = \tan^{-1} \frac{2.1 \times 10^3}{3.01 \times 10^3} = 0.61 \text{ radians} \equiv 34.9°$$

(ii) The input current I_1 splits between the inductor and resistor according to

$$I_2 = \frac{j6.28 \times 10^3}{4.7 \times 10^3 + j6.28 \times 10^3} I_1$$

Thus, the current transfer function $G_I = \frac{I_2}{I_1}$ is

$$G_I = \frac{j6.28}{4.7 + j6.28} = \frac{j6.28(4.7 - j6.28)}{(4.7)^2 + (6.28)^2}$$

which gives

$$G_I = 0.641 + j0.48$$

and so

$$|G_I| = \frac{|I_2|}{|I_1|} = 0.8$$

and

$$\arg G_I = \tan^{-1} \frac{0.48}{0.641} = 0.64 \text{ radians} \equiv 36.8°$$

From the above examples, the reader will by now be aware of the relative simplicity of the phasor approach to the calculation of sinusoidal response when compared with differential equation techniques in the time domain. The relationship between the amplitudes of the input and output sinusoids, together with the phase angle of the output with reference to the input can be found by means of straightforward algebraic manipulations, and for this reason the technique discussed in this chapter has become a standard engineering circuit analysis tool.

3.4 FREQUENCY RESPONSE

If a sinusoidal signal generator is applied to the input of an audio amplifier, and the frequency of the generator is varied, it is found that the human ear responds to signals emitted from the loudspeaker in the approximate range 50 Hz and 16 kHz, although some people (particularly the young) can hear signals having frequencies outside this range. It is important, therefore, that a high fidelity audio amplifier should be capable of reproducing signals in this frequency range without giving undue emphasis to input signal components at particular frequencies, and equally, without attenuating signals at other frequencies in the audible range. In other words, the amplifier should have the same gain at all frequencies within the audible range, that is, a flat *frequency response*. Outside the audible range, the frequency response is of no particular importance since the human ear cannot respond to signals at such frequencies. The amplifier therefore only needs a *passband* which corresponds to that of the ear, namely 50 Hz–16 kHz. In this case the frequency response refers to the gain of the amplifier, e.g., $G_v = |V_2|/|V_1|$, where V_2 and V_1 are the output and input phasors respectively. This is strictly an *amplitude response*, and a typical response for an audio amplifier is shown in Fig. 3.24. In some cases, for example in television or video amplifiers, the variation with frequency of the phase shift between output and input signals is also important, and a plot of phase against frequency gives the *phase response* of the amplifier.

The frequency response of a circuit therefore has two aspects; the amplitude response, which relates the magnitudes of the output and input sinusoidal signals as frequency varies, and the phase response, which indicates the phase shift variation between those signals with frequency. Clearly, both aspects of the frequency response of a circuit may be obtained using the phasor approach. For example, consider the simple RC circuit shown in Fig. 3.25. Using the potential divider rule, the output voltage is given by

$$V_2 = \frac{\dfrac{1}{j\omega C}}{R + \dfrac{1}{j\omega C}} V_1 = \frac{1}{1 + j\omega CR} V_1$$

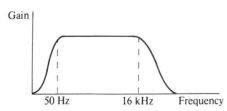

Fig. 3.24 Typical amplitude response of an audio amplifier

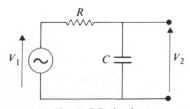

Fig. 3.25 Simple RC circuit

and so

$$\frac{|V_2|}{|V_1|} = \frac{1}{[1+(\omega CR)^2]^{1/2}} \qquad (3.40)$$

$$\phi = -\tan^{-1}(\omega CR) \qquad (3.41)$$

where ϕ is the phase shift between the output and input signals. The frequency response of this circuit may be exhibited by plotting the amplitude and phase responses corresponding to Eq. (3.40) and Eq. (3.41) respectively. We shall consider first the amplitude response given by Eq. (3.40). At very low frequencies for which $(\omega CR)^2 \ll 1$, i.e., $\omega \ll \frac{1}{CR}$, then $\frac{|V_2|}{|V_1|} \approx 1$. At very high frequencies where $\omega \gg \frac{1}{CR}$, then $\frac{|V_2|}{|V_1|} \approx \frac{1}{\omega CR}$, and so the amplitude response halves for every doubling in frequency, or *octave*. At the frequency $\omega = \frac{1}{CR}$, $\frac{|V_2|}{|V_1|} = \frac{1}{\sqrt{2}}$. This shows that there is a wide variation in the amplitude response over any sizeable frequency range. For this reason, frequency responses are usually plotted with a logarithmic scale on the frequency axis, and a logarithmic measure is used for the ratio $\frac{|V_2|}{|V_1|}$. This latter measure has its foundations in the comparison of powers. Suppose that two electrical energy sources dissipate powers P_1 and P_2 in their respective loads. Then a measure of the relative powers is afforded by calculating the quantity $\log_{10}\left(\frac{P_2}{P_1}\right)$, which has been given the units of *bel*. The measure enables a wide range of absolute power ratios to be accommodated by a small range of bels. In fact this unit is rather big for many practical purposes, and use is made of the *decibel* (unit symbol dB), where the relative power in decibels is given by $10\log_{10}\left(\frac{P_2}{P_1}\right)$. If both powers are dissipated in the same load resistance R, then $P_1 = \frac{|V_1|^2}{R}$ and $P_2 = \frac{|V_2|^2}{R}$ where V_1 and V_2 are the phasor voltages across the loads. In this case,

$$10\log_{10}\left(\frac{P_2}{P_1}\right) = 10\log_{10}\left(\frac{|V_2|^2}{|V_1|^2}\right) = 20\log_{10}\left(\frac{|V_2|}{|V_1|}\right)$$

Although the quantity $20\log_{10}\left(\frac{|V_2|}{|V_1|}\right)$ measured in decibels is strictly related to the comparison of power dissipated by two sources in the same load resistance, it has become accepted as the conventional logarithmic measure of the ratio of voltage magnitude. Similarly $20\log_{10}\left(\frac{|I_2|}{|I_1|}\right)$, again in decibels, is used for currents. Table 3.1 shows some commonly occurring ratios expressed in decibels.

Table 3.1

$\dfrac{\|V_2\|}{\|V_1\|}$	$20 \log_{10}\left(\dfrac{\|V_2\|}{\|V_1\|}\right)$ (dB)
10^3	60
10^2	40
10	20
3	9.5
2	6
$\sqrt{2}$	3
1	0
$\dfrac{1}{\sqrt{2}}$	-3
$\dfrac{1}{2}$	-6
$\dfrac{1}{3}$	-9.5
10^{-1}	-20
10^{-2}	-40
10^{-3}	-60

Returning to the amplitude response of the circuit of Fig. 3.25, the gain expressed in dB may be summarized as follows:

$$\omega \ll \frac{1}{CR} \quad : \quad \text{gain } G_v = 20 \log_{10}(1) = 0 \text{ dB} \tag{3.42}$$

$$\omega \gg \frac{1}{CR} \quad : \quad G_v = 20 \log_{10}\left(\frac{1}{\omega CR}\right) = -20 \log_{10} \omega - 20 \log_{10}(CR) \text{ dB} \tag{3.43}$$

$$\omega = \frac{1}{CR} \quad : \quad G_v = 20 \log_{10}\left(\frac{1}{\sqrt{2}}\right) = -3 \text{ dB}$$

The negative signs show that the circuit provides *attenuation* rather than gain. A plot of the response is shown in Fig. 3.26(a). Included on the plot are the asymptotes corresponding to Eq. (3.43). This latter asymptote corresponds to a linear decrease in gain of 6 dB for every doubling in frequency (since $-20 \log_{10}(2\omega) = -20 \log_{10}(2) - 20 \log_{10}(\omega) = -6 - 20 \log_{10}(\omega)$), and thus has a slope of -6 dB/octave, or equivalently, -20 dB/decade, where a decade is a tenfold increase.

The amplitude response shows that the circuit behaves as a *lowpass filter*, since as frequency increases, the output voltage magnitude decreases for a given input magnitude. This is because the capacitor C tends to a short circuit as frequency increases. The frequency $\omega = \omega_b = \dfrac{1}{CR}$ is known variously as the *band edge-*, *cut-off-*, *corner-*, *-3 dB-*, or *half power-frequency* of the circuit, or is also often referred to as the *bandwidth*. The

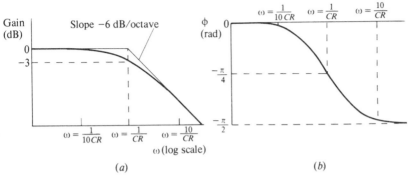

Fig. 3.26 (a) Amplitude, (b) phase response of the simple RC circuit

term 'half-power' refers to the fact that at this frequency, $\dfrac{|V_2|}{|V_1|} = \dfrac{1}{\sqrt{2}}$, i.e.,

$\dfrac{|V_2|^2}{|V_1|^2} = \dfrac{1}{2}$, and so if the output voltage could be applied to some resistive load, it would cause one half of the power to be dissipated which would be obtained if the input voltage were applied to the same load.

The phase response shown in Fig. 3.26(b) is a plot of Eq. (3.41). The phase varies between 0 and $-\dfrac{\pi}{2}$ radians, and is always lagging. For this reason the circuit under consideration is sometimes referred to as a *simple lag*. At the cut-off frequency, $\phi = -\tan^{-1}(1) = -\dfrac{\pi}{4}$, and as the graph shows, for all practical purposes, the phase response can be approximated by

$$\phi = 0, \quad \omega < \dfrac{1}{10CR}$$

$$\phi = -\dfrac{\pi}{2}, \quad \omega > \dfrac{10}{CR}$$

The product CR is, of course, the time constant of the circuit, and in Chapter 2 it was shown that the step response rise time of such a circuit is given by $t_r = 2.2CR$. Writing $CR = \dfrac{1}{\omega_b} = \dfrac{1}{2\pi f_b}$ where f_b is the cut-off frequency in hertz, then $f_b \times t_r = \dfrac{2.2}{(2\pi)} = 0.35$. Thus the product of bandwidth and risetime for a simple lag circuit is a constant. This result is particularly useful, since many practical electronic systems have frequency responses which are similar to the response of a simple lag circuit.

The above discussion has concentrated upon one simple circuit, but has served to emphasize that the amplitude and phase responses together define the frequency response of a circuit. In the case of other circuit configurations, frequency response plotting may often be assisted by the use of similar straight line asymptotes and approximations, and terms such as cut-off frequency, 3 dB frequency and bandwidth are often (but not necessarily) used in the same way.

Example

Plot the frequency response of the circuit shown in Fig. 3.27.

The resistor R_2 and the inductor are in parallel, and so have a combined impedance of $(R_2 \cdot j\omega L)/(R_2 + j\omega L)$. Using the potential divider rule, the output voltage is given by

$$V_2 = \frac{\dfrac{j\omega L R_2}{(R_2 + j\omega L)}}{R_1 + \dfrac{j\omega L R_2}{R_2 + j\omega L}} V_1 = \frac{j\omega L R_2}{R_1 R_2 + j\omega L (R_1 + R_2)} V_2$$

This may be written as

$$V_2 = \frac{R_2}{R_1 + R_2} \cdot \frac{j\omega L}{\dfrac{R_1 R_2}{R_1 + R_2} + j\omega L} = \frac{R_2}{R_1 + R_2} \cdot \frac{j\omega \dfrac{L}{R'}}{1 + j\omega \dfrac{L}{R'}} V_1 \qquad (3.44)$$

where

$$R' = \frac{R_1 R_2}{R_1 + R_2}$$

Eq. (3.44) gives

$$\frac{|V_2|}{|V_1|} = \frac{R_2}{R_1 + R_2} \cdot \frac{\dfrac{\omega L}{R'}}{\left[1 + \left(\dfrac{\omega L}{R'}\right)^2\right]^{1/2}} \qquad (3.45)$$

$$\phi = \frac{\pi}{2} - \tan^{-1}\left(\frac{\omega L}{R'}\right) \qquad (3.46)$$

where ϕ is the phase angle between V_2 and V_1.

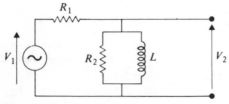

Fig. 3.27 Circuit example

Eq. (3.45), when expressed in dB, may be written as

$$20 \log_{10} \left(\frac{|V_2|}{|V_1|} \right) = 20 \log_{10} \left(\frac{R_2}{R_1 + R_2} \right) + 20 \log_{10} \frac{\dfrac{\omega L}{R'}}{\left[1 + \left(\dfrac{\omega L}{R'} \right)^2 \right]^{1/2}}$$

The first term on the right hand side is constant with frequency and will have a value depending on R_1 and R_2. Let this be $\mathscr{L}$ dB where $\mathscr{L} \leq 0$. The second term corresponds to a gain G which varies with frequency, and as with the simple lag circuit, three values of frequency may be considered, as follows:

$$\omega \ll \frac{R'}{L} \quad : \quad G = 20 \log_{10} \left(\frac{\omega L}{R'} \right) \text{dB}$$

$$\omega = \frac{R'}{L} \quad : \quad G = 20 \log_{10} \left(\frac{1}{\sqrt{2}} \right) = -3 \text{ dB}$$

$$\omega \gg \frac{R'}{L} \quad : \quad G = 20 \log_{10} (1) = 0 \text{ dB}$$

The amplitude response is shown in Fig. 3.28(a), and is seen to selectively attenuate low frequency signals below the cut off frequency $\omega = \dfrac{R'}{L}$. The circuit therefore provides a *high pass* filter response. This is because the inductor behaves as a short circuit for low frequency signals.

Fig. 3.28(b) is a plot of the phase response obtained from Eq. (3.46). This is seen to be a *leading* response, since the phase is positive in the range 0 to $\dfrac{\pi}{2}$ radians.

Many electronic circuits, including filters and equalisers, are designed to have specific frequency responses which provide either gain or attenuation

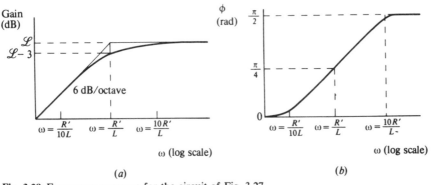

Fig. 3.28 Frequency response for the circuit of Fig. 3.27

over certain frequency bands according to the requirement. Responses may be obtained having very steep transitions between the *passbands* and *stopbands* over which input signals are transmitted or attenuated. These circuits exploit the frequency varying impedances of inductors and capacitors, and in Chapter 4 we shall be considering further simple cases of frequency response.

3.5 SUMMARY

This chapter has been concerned with the evaluation of the steady state sinusoidal response of linear circuits. By argument and example, it has been shown that the application of a sinusoidal signal to such a circuit results in a response or output having two components. The natural or transient response resulting from the application of the sinusoid will, for most practical purposes, decay to zero relatively quickly, leaving the circuit in a steady state. The steady state component of the response will be sinusoidal, having an amplitude related to the amplitude of the input, but also having some phase shift with respect to that input.

As a means of overcoming the need to derive the differential equation describing the circuit behaviour in order to find the steady state sinusoidal response, it has been shown that the sinusoidal voltages and currents around a circuit may be represented (through their real axis projection) by vectors rotating about the origin of the Argand vector diagram with the same angular frequency as the input signal. Recalling that it is the relative amplitudes and phase shifts of these vectors which are of interest, phase vectors or phasors were introduced, these being frozen versions of their spinning vector counterparts. There is therefore a one to one correspondence between a phasor and the time domain sinusoid which it represents, a correspondance which ensures that Kirchhoff's Voltage and Current Laws apply for phasors in the same way as time domain signals. Since the phasors embody the amplitudes and phases of time domain signals for a particular frequency, the manipulation of phasors is said to be carried out in the frequency domain. In this domain, the relationships between the current and voltage phasors pertaining to the basic components of resistance, capacitance, and inductance are found to be algebraic, this single fact providing motivation for the approach, since as we have seen, sinusoidal response may be found from the solution of algebraic rather than differential equations.

Finally it has been seen that the manner in which the amplitude and phase relationships between sinusoidal input and output signals vary with frequency is known as the frequency response, and gives an indication of the frequency selective properties of the circuit.

Problems

1. Determine the output voltage $v_o(t)$ in the circuit shown in Fig. 3.29 when an input voltage $v = V_m \sin \omega t$ is applied at time $t = 0$ s.

$$\left(\text{Answer: } \left[V_m \frac{\omega T e^{-t/T}}{\omega^2 T^2 + 1} + \frac{1}{[\omega^2 T^2 + 1]^{1/2}} \sin (\omega t + \phi) \right], \ \phi = \tan^{-1}(-\omega T), \ T = RC \right)$$

2. Find the phasor equivalents for the following signals:

   (i) $3 \cos \left(\omega t + \dfrac{\pi}{6} \right)$, (ii) $-2 \sin \left(\omega t + \dfrac{\pi}{8} \right)$. Express the results in both polar and rectangular form.

   $$\left(\text{Answer: (i) } 3 \underline{/\frac{\pi}{6}}, \ 2.6 + j1.5; \text{ (ii) } 2 \underline{/\frac{5\pi}{8}}, \ -0.765 + j1.848 \right)$$

3. Two sinusoidal signals of frequency 100 Hz have phasor representations given by (i) $V = 4e^{j\pi/5}$, (ii) $I = 5 + j12$. Find the corresponding time domain signals.

   $$\left(\text{Answer: (i) } 4 \cos \left(200\pi t + \frac{\pi}{5} \right), \text{ (ii) } 13 \cos \left(200 \ \pi t + 1.176 \right) \right)$$

4. A phasor current $I = 5e^{j\pi/4}$ flows through an impedance $Z = (3 + j4)\Omega$. Find the voltage developed across this impedance.
   (Answer: $(-3.54 + j24.75)$ V)

5. An admittance has conductive part 2.5 mS, and susceptive part—4 mS. Find the resistive and reactive parts of the corresponding impedance.
   (Answer: 112.4 Ω, 179.8 Ω)

6. Find the impedance of the circuit shown in Fig. 3.30 at 1 MHz.
   (Answer: $(24.7 - j92.4)\Omega$)

7. Derive the conditions under which the circuit shown in Fig. 3.31 has an impedance which is independent of frequency.

   $$\left(\text{Answer: } R_1 = R_2, \frac{L}{C} = R_1^2 \right)$$

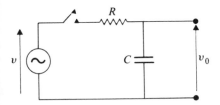

Fig. 3.29 Circuit example for problem 1

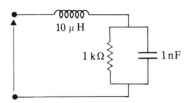

Fig. 3.30 Circuit example for problem 6

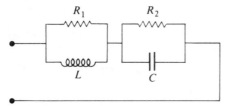

Fig. 3.31 Circuit example for problem 7

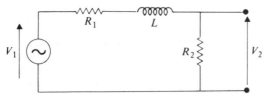

Fig. 3.32 Circuit example for problem 8

8. Find the magnitude and phase of the output voltage V_2 in Fig. 3.32 in terms of the input voltage V_1 at frequency ω rad/s.

$$\left(\text{Answer: } \frac{|V_2|}{|V_1|} = \frac{R_2}{[(R_1 + R_2)^2 + \omega^2 L^2]^{1/2}}, \quad \phi = -\tan^{-1}\left(\frac{\omega L}{R_1 + R_2}\right)\right)$$

9. Determine the bandwidth ω_b of the circuit in Fig. 3.32 and calculate the attenuation at $2\omega_b$, $4\omega_b$, $10\omega_b$ and $100\omega_b$ in dB, relative to the d.c. attenuation.

$$\left(\text{Answer: } \omega_b = \frac{(R_1 + R_2)}{L}, \text{ 7 dB, 12.3 dB, 20.0 dB, 40.0 dB}\right)$$

10. Calculate the amplitude and phase of the output voltage in the circuit shown in Fig. 3.33 at frequency $\omega = 10^4$ rad/s.
(Answer: 0.353 V, −90°)

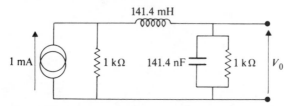

Fig. 3.33 Circuit example for problem 9

4
TUNED CIRCUITS

In this chapter we shall use knowledge gained from the previous chapters to consider an important class of circuits, known as *tuned circuits*. In particular we shall find the techniques of phasor analysis particularly useful in investigating the phenomenon of *resonance* in these circuits. This phenomenon becomes apparent where a circuit is connected to signal source whose frequency is close to the frequency of the natural, or transient response of the circuit. A familiar mechanical analogy is that of the simple pendulum which can be kept swinging at its natural frequency by applying a force to the pendulum bob at the start of each swing. While initial energy must be supplied to set the pendulum in motion, only that required to make up for energy expended in overcoming air resistance, and so on, needs to be subsequently provided. Resonant effects are also apparent in motor cars, where annoying vibrations are often heard at particular road or engine speeds as various components in the bodywork of the car are excited near to their natural frequencies, the effect being particularly noticeable when the excitation (due to the road surface, or engine speed) coincides with the natural frequency.

4.1   ENERGY STORAGE IN TUNED CIRCUITS

To begin the study of tuned circuits, we may consider again the series LCR circuit shown in Fig. 4.1, driven from a sinusoidal voltage source.

Assume that in the steady state, a time domain current $i = I_m \cos \omega t$ flows in this circuit. Then the energy ξ_L stored in the inductor at time t is given by:

$$\xi_L = \frac{1}{2} Li^2 = \frac{LI_m^2}{2} \cos^2 \omega t \tag{4.1}$$

Now the voltage across the capacitor is

$$v_C = \frac{1}{C} \int_0^t i \, dt = \frac{I_m}{\omega C} \sin \omega t$$

and so the energy ξ_C stored in the capacitor is

$$\xi_C = \frac{1}{2} Cv_C^2 = \frac{I_m^2}{2\omega^2 C} \sin^2 \omega t = \frac{I_m^2}{2\omega^2 C} (1 - \cos^2 \omega t) \tag{4.2}$$

The total energy stored in the components L and C (the *reactive components*) is, from Eq. (4.1) and Eq. (4.2)

$$\xi_{LC} = \frac{I_m^2}{2\omega^2 C} + \frac{I_m^2}{2} \cos^2 \omega t \left(L - \frac{1}{\omega^2 C} \right) \tag{4.3}$$

Eq. (4.3) shows that the total energy stored by the reactive components has, at a particular frequency, a constant part, and a part which is pulsating with time. Of particular interest is the behaviour at the frequency $\omega = \omega_0$ at

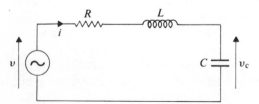

Fig. 4.1 LCR circuit

which $\left(L - \dfrac{1}{\omega^2 C}\right)$ is zero, i.e., $\omega_0 = \dfrac{1}{\sqrt{LC}}$. In this case,

$$\xi_{LC} = \frac{I_m^2}{2\omega_0^2 C} = \frac{I_m^2 L}{2} \tag{4.4}$$

Eq. (4.4) shows that the total energy stored in the reactive components at this frequency is constant with time. However, Eq. (4.1) and Eq. (4.2) indicate that the energy in the capacitor and inductor separately are varying with time. The situation is shown in Fig. 4.2. It can only be concluded that the total energy is continually being transferred from the inductor to the capacitor, and vice-versa. All the energy will reside in the capacitor when the voltage across it is maximum, while all the energy will be stored in the inductor when the current reaches a maximum value. Thus, after the input sinusoidal source has been applied to the circuit, and the transients have died away leaving the steady state current i, the energy $\dfrac{I_m^2 L}{2}$ stored in the reactive components will have been established. The only energy then supplied from the source will be that which is dissipated as heat in the resistor. As far as the source is concerned, the LCR circuit will therefore appear to be resistive at this frequency, and so the current i and the voltage v may be expected to be in phase. This expectation will be confirmed in the next section.

At this frequency, $\omega_0 = \dfrac{1}{\sqrt{LC}}$, the current in the circuit is in phase with the voltage, and the circuit is said to be *resonant*. In the context of this simple tuned circuit we have seen that at the *resonant frequency* ω_0, the total energy in the reactive components is constant, and is shared in time between the inductor and the capacitor. The time varying proportions of energy may be thought of as being located at any instant in the electric field of the capacitor, and the magnetic field of the inductor.

Since the only energy supplied to the circuit at resonance is that supplied to the resistor, and this resistor will often represent the winding losses of

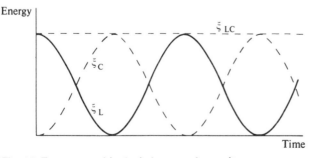

Fig. 4.2 Energy stored in the inductor and capacitor

the inductor (which in an ideal inductor should be zero), it is of interest to consider the ratio of energy stored in the reactive components to the energy dissipated in the resistor over one cycle of the applied waveform. This ratio will give an indication of the *circuit quality factor*.

The energy dissipated over each cycle of duration $2\pi/\omega$ seconds is given by

$$\xi_R = \int_0^{2\pi/\omega_0} i^2 R \, dt = I_m^2 R \int_0^{2\pi/\omega_0} \cos^2 \omega_0 t \, dt$$

$$= \frac{I_m^2 R}{2} \int_0^{2\pi/\omega_0} (\cos 2\omega_0 t + 1) \, dt = \frac{I_m^2 R}{2} \left[\frac{1}{2\omega_0} \sin 2\omega_0 t + t \right]_0^{2\pi/\omega_0} \quad (4.5)$$

i.e.,

$$\xi_R = \pi \frac{I_m R}{\omega_0}$$

Noting Eq. (4.4) and Eq. (4.5)

$$\frac{\xi_{LC}}{\xi_R} = \frac{I_m^2 L}{2} \cdot \frac{\omega_0}{\pi I_m^2 R}$$

$$= \frac{\omega_0 L}{2\pi R} = \frac{Q}{2\pi} \quad (4.6)$$

where $Q = \dfrac{\omega_0 L}{R}$ is the *circuit quality factor*. Alternatively, since R is often associated with the winding resistance of the inductor, Q is known as the quality factor of the inductor at the frequency ω_0.

4.2   RESONANCE

In the last section, an investigation of the energy stored in a tuned circuit served as an introduction to the phenomenon of resonance. To study this further, we may consider the phasor analysis of the circuit of Fig. 4.1 which is redrawn in Fig. 4.3 with the phasor quantities annotated.

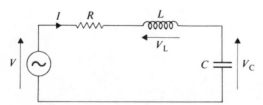

Fig. 4.3 Circuit of Fig. 4.1 with phasor variables

At a frequency ω,

$$I = \frac{V}{R + j\omega L + \frac{1}{j\omega C}} = \frac{V}{R + j\left(\omega L - \frac{1}{\omega C}\right)} \tag{4.7}$$

Thus

$$|I| = \frac{|V|}{\left\{R^2 + \left(\omega L - \frac{1}{\omega C}\right)^2\right\}^{1/2}} \tag{4.8}$$

$$\phi = \tan^{-1}\frac{\left(\omega L - \frac{1}{\omega C}\right)}{R} \tag{4.9}$$

where ϕ is the phase angle between the sinusoidal waveforms of the current and the applied voltage.

Eq. (4.8) and Eq. (4.9) are plotted against frequency in Fig. 4.4 and Fig. 4.5 respectively.

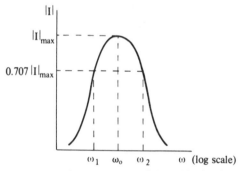

Fig. 4.4 Amplitude response of the LCR circuit

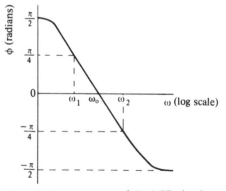

Fig. 4.5 Phase response of the LCR circuit

At frequencies below the resonant frequency, the capacitive reactance dominates in Eq. (4.7), and a leading phase shift results as seen in Fig. 4.5. The series tuned circuit is then said to be capacitive. At frequencies above resonance on the other hand, the inductive reactance becomes dominant, giving a lagging phase shift, the circuit then being termed inductive. At the resonant frequency $\omega = \omega_0 = \dfrac{1}{\sqrt{LC}}$ the capacitive and inductive reactances cancel, that is $\omega L - \dfrac{1}{\omega L} = 0$, and Eq. (4.7) shows that the current I is then defined by the resistance R. Thus, at resonance, the tuned circuit is resistive, and the phase shift ϕ is zero as shown in Fig. 4.5. This confirms the statement made in the last section. Consideration of Eq. (4.8) shows that the current magnitude increases as the resonant frequency is approached, as shown in Fig. 4.4, and indeed the maximum current occurs at resonance, and is given by $|I|_{max} = |V|/R$. It is left as an exercise to the reader to confirm that this is the maximum by setting the differential $\dfrac{d|I|}{d\omega}$ obtained from Eq. (4.8) to zero in the usual way. The impedance of the tuned circuit at its resonant frequency is known as its *dynamic impedance*, and in this case Eq. (4.7) shows that this is the resistance R.

At resonance, the voltage V_L across the inductor is given by

$$V_L = j\omega_0 LI = j\omega_0 L \frac{V}{R}$$

i.e.,

$$V_L = jQV \tag{4.10}$$

Eq. (4.10) shows that the inductor voltage V_L leads the applied voltage by $90°$, and has a magnitude which is Q times greater. In practice Q can have a value of several hundred for wound inductors, and so voltage magnification may be obtained with the tuned circuit. Turning to the capacitor, and bearing in mind that $\omega_0 L = \dfrac{1}{\omega_0 C}$ at resonance,

$$V_C = -j\frac{1}{\omega_0 C}I = -j\omega_0 L \frac{V}{R}$$

i.e.,

$$V_C = -jQV \tag{4.11}$$

Again, voltage magnification may be obtained, in this case the capacitor voltage lagging the applied voltage by $90°$. Eq. (4.10) and Eq. (4.11) indicate that the voltage drops across the series connection of the inductor and capacitor will sum to zero, so that the applied voltage V appears across the resistor, and this is in keeping with our previous remarks.

A further definition of Q which has resulted from the above development is that it is the *voltage magnification factor* of the series tuned circuit. In fact, yet another useful interpretation of Q may be obtained, as we shall now see.

At resonance, the power dissipated in the resistor is $|I|_{max}^2 R$. (This assumes that r.m.s. values are used for the phasor voltages and currents.) This power will have dropped by one half at the frequencies at which $|I| = 0.707|I|_{max}$. These frequencies are shown as ω_1 and ω_2 in Fig. 4.4, and may be found as the frequencies at which

$$\left(\omega L - \frac{1}{\omega C}\right) = \pm R \qquad (4.12)$$

since then, in Eq. (4.8),

$$|I| = \frac{|V|}{\{R^2 + R^2\}^{1/2}} = \frac{|V|}{\sqrt{2}R} = 0.707|I|_{max}$$

From Eq. (4.12),

$$\omega^2 LC \mp \omega CR - 1 = 0$$

or

$$\omega^2 \mp \frac{\omega R}{L} - \frac{1}{LC} = 0 \qquad (4.13)$$

Noting $\omega_o = \frac{1}{\sqrt{LC}}$, and $Q = \frac{\omega_o L}{R}$, Eq. (4.13) may be written as

$$\omega^2 \mp \frac{\omega \omega_o}{Q} - \omega_o^2 = 0$$

from which

$$\omega = \frac{\pm \frac{\omega_o}{Q} \pm \left(\frac{\omega_o^2}{Q^2} + 4\omega_o^2\right)^{1/2}}{2} = \pm \frac{\omega_o}{2Q} \pm \frac{\omega_o}{2Q}(1 + 4Q^2)^{1/2} \qquad (4.14)$$

A moments thought shows that only two of the four possible solutions available from Eq. (4.14) will give positive values of ω, and these are

$$\left. \begin{aligned} \omega_1 &= -\frac{\omega_o}{2Q} + \frac{\omega_o}{2Q}(1 + 4Q^2)^{1/2} \\ \omega_2 &= +\frac{\omega_o}{2Q} + \frac{\omega_o}{2Q}(1 + 4Q^2)^{1/2} \end{aligned} \right\} \qquad (4.15)$$

The frequencies ω_1 and ω_2 are known as the *half power, band edge,* or $-3\ dB$ frequencies $\left(\text{since } 20 \log_{10}\left(\frac{0.707|I|_{max}}{|I|_{max}}\right) = -3\ \text{dB}\right)$. Their difference,

$\omega_1 - \omega_2$ is the *bandwidth* BW of the tuned circuit frequency response. From Eqs. (4.15),

$$BW = \omega_2 - \omega_1 = \frac{\omega_o}{2Q} + \frac{\omega_o}{2Q} = \frac{\omega_o}{Q}$$

i.e.,

$$Q = \frac{\omega_o}{BW}$$

Thus Q is also given by the ratio of the resonant frequency to the bandwidth, and gives a measure of the sharpness or *selectivity* of the response curve. Substituting Eq. (4.12) into Eq. (4.9), it will be seen that a phase shift of $\pm \frac{\pi}{4}$ radians is obtained at the $-3\,\text{dB}$ frequencies, and so the phase response around the resonant frequency will be expected to become steeper as the Q is increased and the bandwidth becomes smaller. These points are exemplified in Fig. 4.6 and Fig. 4.7 which show responses for

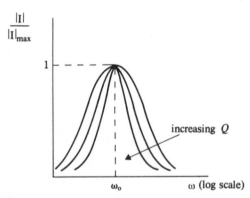

Fig. 4.6 Amplitude response variation with Q

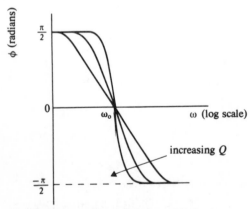

Fig. 4.7 Phase response variation with Q

arious values of Q. The scale of the magnitude curves is normalized so hat all the curves have the same maximum value.

The reader may have noticed an apparent symmetry in the magnitude nd phase curves about the resonant frequency, and that a logarithmic requency scale has been used for all the graphs shown in Figs. 4.4 to 4.7. 'his is because the magnitude and phase responses have a geometric ymmetry as functions of ω, which becomes an arithmetic symmetry when og ω is used. For example, Eqs. (4.15) give

$$\omega_1\omega_2 = \left[\frac{\omega_0}{2Q}(1+4Q^2)^{1/2} - \frac{\omega_0}{2Q}\right]\left[\frac{\omega_0}{2Q}(1+4Q^2)^{1/2} + \frac{\omega_0}{2Q}\right]$$

$$= \frac{\omega_0^2}{4Q^2}(1+4Q^2) - \frac{\omega_0^2}{4Q^2} = \omega_0^2$$

nd so

$$\omega_0 = \sqrt{\omega_1\omega_2}$$

nd

$$\log \omega_0 = \frac{1}{2}(\log \omega_1 + \log \omega_2)$$

This last equation shows that on a logarithmic scale, the resonant frequency ω_0 will lie half way between the band edge frequencies ω_1 and ω_2.

Many circuits exhibit the phenomenon of resonance and frequency selectivity discussed above. Another simple circuit is the parallel tuned circuit shown in Fig. 4.8. To find the resonant frequency of this circuit, we need only note that at resonance the current and voltage in the circuit will be in phase, and the circuit will then appear resistive. It is sufficient therefore to find the frequency at which the imaginary part of the impedance (or admittance) of the circuit is zero. For this circuit, the admittance Y proves to be the most convenient, and

$$Y = \frac{1}{R} + j\omega C + \frac{1}{j\omega L} = \frac{1}{R} + j\left(\omega C - \frac{1}{\omega L}\right) \tag{4.16}$$

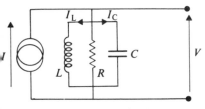

Fig. 4.8 Parallel resonant circuit

and the imaginary part of Eq. (4.16) will be zero when $\omega = \omega_0 = \dfrac{1}{\sqrt{LC}}$. The dynamic impedance of the circuit is then R. The voltage appearing across the parallel tuned circuit is obtained from Eq. (4.16), and is

$$V = \frac{I}{Y} = \frac{I}{\dfrac{1}{R} + j\left(\omega C - \dfrac{1}{\omega L}\right)} \tag{4.17}$$

The magnitude and phase characteristics obtained from Eq. (4.17) are of the form shown in Fig. 4.6 and Fig. 4.7, the magnitude curve in this case being that of the relative voltage $\dfrac{|V|}{|V|_{max}}$ developed across the circuit, while the phase shift is that of the voltage with reference to the applied current. As Eq. (4.17) confirms, a parallel tuned circuit is inductive below the resonant frequency and capacitive above it, in contrast with the series circuit.

To find the Q factor of the parallel tuned circuit, note that at resonance the average power dissipated in the circuit is $|I|^2R$ (remember r.m.s. values are being used for the phasor quantities). Thus, the energy ξ_R supplied to the circuit over one cycle is

$$\xi_R = |I|^2 R \frac{2\pi}{\omega_0} \tag{4.18}$$

Now the energy ξ_{LC} stored in the reactive components will all reside in the capacitor when the instantaneous voltage across it is maximum. This maximum voltage will be $\sqrt{2}|I|R$, since $\sqrt{2}|I|$ is the peak instantaneous value of the applied current. The reactive energy is therefore

$$\xi_{LC} = \frac{1}{2} C(\sqrt{2}|I|R)^2 \tag{4.19}$$

Noting Eqs. (4.6), (4.18) and (4.19) give

$$Q = 2\pi \times \frac{\xi_{LC}}{\xi_R} = \frac{2\pi \times |I|^2 CR^2}{|I|^2 R \dfrac{2\pi}{\omega_0}} = \omega_0 CR$$

Alternatively, since $\omega_0 C = \dfrac{1}{\omega_0 L}$, $Q = \dfrac{R}{\omega_0 L}$. Thus the Q factor of the parallel tuned circuit is the inverse of that of the series tuned circuit. In this case, to obtain a high Q, the resistor R should be made as high as possible.

In a manner similar to the series tuned circuit, it turns out that *current* magnification can occur in the parallel tuned circuit. At resonance, the voltage developed across the circuit $V = IR$, and this will have a maximum amplitude. The capacitor current $I_C = j\omega_0 CV = j\omega_0 CRI$, that is $I_C = jQI$. Thus the capacitor current leads the applied current by 90°, and has a magnitude Q times greater. A similar current, but having opposite sign, flows in the inductor at resonance. As might be expected, the Q factor also relates the resonant frequency to the bandwidth of the parallel circuit response, in just the same way as we found for the series tuned circuit.

In fact, the parallel tuned circuit shown in Fig. 4.8 has little direct practical relevance, since although the resistor R may be associated with dielectric loss in the capacitor, and we may define $Q = \omega_o CR$ as a quality factor for the capacitor, it is the series winding loss of the inductor, neglected in this circuit, which usually has the greatest practical effect. The following example discusses a circuit which takes account of this.

Example

The circuit shown in Fig. 4.9 models a practical tuned circuit in which capacitor dielectric loss has been ignored. Calculate (i) the resonant frequency, (ii) the dynamic impedance, (iii) the Q factor for this circuit. Take $L = 1\,\text{mH}$, $r = 10\,\Omega$, $C = 1\,\text{nF}$.

The admittance of the circuit is

$$Y = j\omega C + \frac{1}{r + j\omega L} = j\omega C + \frac{(r - j\omega L)}{r^2 + \omega^2 L^2}$$

$$= \frac{r}{r^2 + \omega^2 L^2} + j\left(\omega C - \frac{\omega L}{r^2 + \omega^2 L^2}\right) \tag{4.20}$$

At resonance, the imaginary part of the admittance will be zero, so

$$C - \frac{L}{r^2 + \omega_o^2 L^2} = 0$$

i.e.,

$$r^2 + \omega_o^2 L^2 = \frac{L}{C} \tag{4.21}$$

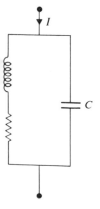

Fig. 4.9 Practical parallel tuned circuit

$$\therefore \qquad \omega_o = \sqrt{\frac{1}{LC} - \frac{r^2}{L^2}} \qquad (4.22)$$

Substituting the given values,

$$\omega_o = \sqrt{\frac{1}{10^{-3} \times 10^{-9}} - \frac{10^2}{10^{-6}}} = \sqrt{10^{12} - 10^4} \simeq 10^6 \, \text{rad/s}$$

From Eq. (4.20), the dynamic impedance Z_d is

$$Z_d = \frac{r^2 + \omega_o^2 L^2}{r}$$

Using Eq. (4.21), this becomes

$$Z_d = \frac{L}{Cr} \qquad (4.23)$$

With the present values, $Z_d = \dfrac{10^{-3}}{(10^{-9} \times 10)} = 100 \, \text{k}\Omega$. Thus, at the resonant frequency, the circuit behaves as a resistor of value $100 \, \text{k}\Omega$. We may find the Q factor from energy considerations. At resonance, the average power dissipated in the circuit, assuming an applied current I is $|I|^2 \cdot L/Cr$. The energy ξ_R supplied during one cycle is then

$$\xi_R = |I|^2 \cdot \frac{L}{Cr} \cdot \frac{2\pi}{\omega_o} \qquad (4.24)$$

The maximum instantaneous voltage appearing across the capacitor is $\sqrt{2}|I| \dfrac{L}{Cr}$, and therefore the reactive energy (which at that instant will all be stored in the capacitor) is

$$\xi_{LC} = \frac{1}{2} C \left(\sqrt{2}|I| \cdot \frac{L}{Cr} \right)^2 \qquad (4.25)$$

Using Eq. (4.24) and Eq. (4.25),

$$Q = 2\pi \cdot \frac{\xi_{LC}}{\xi_R} = \frac{2\pi \cdot |I|^2 C \left(\dfrac{L}{Cr}\right)^2}{|I|^2 \left(\dfrac{L}{Cr}\right)\left(\dfrac{2\pi}{\omega_o}\right)} = \frac{\omega_o L}{r} \qquad (4.26)$$

Eq. (4.26) shows that the Q factor of this parallel tuned circuit is of the same form as that for the series tuned circuit—it is the ratio of the inductive reactance to the inductor series resistance at resonance. For this particular case, $Q = \dfrac{10^6 \times 10^{-3}}{10} = 100$.

Whereas the resonant frequency for the previous two circuits was simply $\omega_o = \dfrac{1}{\sqrt{LC}}$, Eq. (4.22) shows that for the present circuit, ω_o will be a little ss than this. However using Eq. (4.26), Eq. (4.22) may be written as

$$\omega_o = \sqrt{\frac{1}{LC} - \frac{\omega_o^2}{Q^2}}$$

olving for ω_o, we find

$$\omega_o = \frac{1}{\sqrt{LC}} \cdot \frac{Q}{\sqrt{1+Q^2}}$$

nd providing $Q^2 \gg 1$, $\omega_o^2 \simeq \frac{1}{LC}$ in line with the other circuits. Using this pproximation, the expression for Z_d in Eq. (4.23) may be manipulated to ive

$$Z_d = \frac{L}{Cr} = \frac{1}{LC} \cdot \frac{L^2}{r} = \frac{\omega_o^2 L^2}{r} = Q^2 r$$

For many practical purposes, therefore, the circuit of Fig. 4.9 behaves imilarly to that shown in Fig. 4.10, where the series resistor r has been eplaced by a resistor of value $Q^2 r$ in parallel with the reactive components.

As a final point, while the series tuned circuit exhibits its minimum mpedance magnitude at resonance (since the current has its maximum implitude at that frequency), and the parallel tuned circuit of Fig. 4.8 and Fig. 4.10 has its maximum impedance magnitude at ω_o, this is only ipproximately true for the circuit of Fig. 4.9. In fact, this circuit exhibits a naximum impedance magnitude at a frequency which can be shown to be given by

$$\omega = \omega_o \left\{ \left[\left(1 + \frac{1}{Q^2}\right)\left(1 + \frac{3}{Q^2}\right) \right]^{1/2} - \frac{1}{Q^2} \right\}$$

This frequency is above the resonant frequency, but again, providing $Q^2 \gg 1$, then $\omega \simeq \omega_o$.

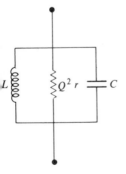

Fig. 4.10 Equivalent circuit for Fig. 4.9

As the number of reactive components increases in a circuit, the number of resonant frequencies also increases. For example, the circuit shown in Fig. 4.11 is a realistic electrical model of a crystal resonator which is shown symbolically in Fig. 4.12. The resonator may be manufactured by vacuum deposition of metallic electrodes onto a small slice of quartz which is cut from a quartz crystal in a plane which makes a particular angle with the crystal axes. When the crystal is excited electrically, mechanical resonances take place giving rise to behaviour which can be modelled by the electrical equivalent circuit shown in Fig. 4.11, the particular electrical characteristics being determined by the crystal angle chosen. For example, an AT-cut crystal for application at about 1 MHz may have $L = 4H$, $C_s = 6$ mpF $(6 \times 10^{-3}$ pF$)$, $R = 100 \, \Omega$, and $C_p = 1.5$ pF. Note the extremely high values of L and the low value of C_s. The value for the parallel capacitor C_p will be influenced practically by the interelectrode capacitance of the crystal, and the wiring capacitance of the circuit in which it is connected. Crystal resonators find particular application in highly selective electrical filters, and high stability oscillator circuits.

To investigate the resonant frequencies of the resonator, we begin by

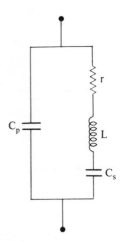

Fig. 4.11 Crystal resonator model

Fig. 4.12 Symbol for a crystal resonator

writing an expression for the admittance of the circuit in Fig. 4.11. This is

$$Y = j\omega C_p + \cfrac{1}{r + j\left(\omega L - \cfrac{1}{\omega C_s}\right)}$$

$$= \cfrac{r}{r^2 + \left(\omega L - \cfrac{1}{\omega C_s}\right)^2} + j\left[\omega C_p - \cfrac{\left(\omega L - \cfrac{1}{\omega C_s}\right)}{r^2 + \left(\omega L - \cfrac{1}{\omega C_s}\right)^2}\right] \qquad (4.27)$$

Resonance occurs when the imaginary part of Eq. (4.27) is zero, i.e.,

$$\omega C_p\left[r^2 + \left(\omega L - \frac{1}{\omega C_s}\right)^2\right] - \left(\omega L - \frac{1}{\omega C_s}\right) = 0$$

Expanding and collecting terms, this gives

$$\omega C_p r^2 + \left(\omega L - \frac{1}{\omega C_s}\right)\left[\omega C_p\left(\omega L - \frac{1}{\omega C_s}\right) - 1\right] = 0 \qquad (4.28)$$

Providing the term $\omega C_p r^2$ is small (and this is justifiable for our purposes), it can be ignored. Two resonant frequencies can then be found directly from Eq. (4.28). The first is given by $\left(\omega L - \frac{1}{\omega C_s}\right) = 0$, i.e.,

$$\omega_s = \frac{1}{\sqrt{LC_s}} \qquad (4.29)$$

where $\omega = \omega_s$ is the *series resonant frequency*. It is the frequency at which the series circuit LrC_s is at resonance. At this frequency, the dynamic impedance is therefore r, as Eq. (4.27) confirms. The second resonant frequency is given by

$$\omega C_p\left(\omega L - \frac{1}{\omega C_s}\right) - 1 = 0$$

which yields

$$\omega_p = \sqrt{\frac{C_s + C_p}{LC_sC_p}} = \omega_s\sqrt{1 + \frac{C_s}{C_p}} \qquad (4.30)$$

Here $\omega = \omega_p$ is known as the *parallel resonant frequency*. The dynamic impedance at this frequency may be found from Eq. (4.27), and is found (assuming r to be small, and $C_s \ll C_p$) to be given approximately by $\dfrac{LC_s}{C_p^2 r}$.

Using the typical values for the components given previously, from Eq. (4.29)

$$\omega_s = \frac{1}{\sqrt{4 \times 6 \times 10^{-15}}} = 6.455 \times 10^6 \text{ rad/s } (\equiv 1.027 \text{ MHz})$$

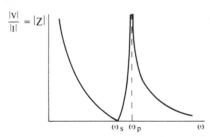

Fig. 4.13 Variation of impedance magnitude with frequency for a crystal resonator

The dynamic impedance at this frequency will be 100 Ω. The Q factor of this series tuned circuit is $Q = \omega_s \dfrac{L}{r} = 6.455 \times 10^6 \times \dfrac{4}{100} \simeq 258\,000!$ This is a staggering figure, which could never be realised with a practical wound inductor. Using Eq. (4.30), the parallel resonant frequency is given by

$$\omega_p = \omega_s \sqrt{1 + \frac{6 \times 10^{-15}}{1.5 \times 10^{-12}}} = 1.002\omega_s = 6.468 \text{ rad/s} \; (\equiv 1.029 \text{ MHz})$$

The dynamic impedance at the parallel resonant frequency is $\dfrac{4 \times 6 \times 10^{-15}}{[(1.5 \times 10^{-12})^2 \times 100]} = 106.7$ MΩ. We see that the series and parallel resonant frequencies are very close together, and yet the crystal impedance has changed by many orders of magnitude between these frequencies. Fig. 4.13 shows the way in which $|Z|$, the magnitude of the impedance varies with frequency and stresses this rapid rate of change between ω_s and ω_p.

4.3 APPLICATIONS OF TUNED CIRCUITS

We have seen in the last section that tuned circuits have two major properties. On the one hand, they have frequency selective characteristics which can exhibit voltage or current magnification, while on the other they are resistive at their resonant frequencies. It is either or both of these two properties which are used in all applications of tuned circuits.

An applications example which uses the frequency selective properties of tuned circuits is that of the domestic radio receiver. A multitude of broadcast radio signals are radiated from commercial transmitting stations over a wide frequency spectrum, and it is the job of the domestic receiver to select one among the many stations according to the choice of the listener. Fig. 4.14 shows a rather simplified diagrammatic version of a radio receiver which stresses the function of the input tuned circuit. The aerial will pick up broadcast signals over the frequency band for which it is designed, and the aerial signal currents will develop a voltage across the input tuned circuit according to the typical response curve shown in Fig.

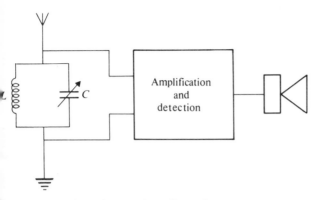

Fig. 4.14 Simplified diagram of a radio receiver

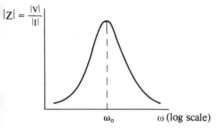

Fig. 4.15 Tuned circuit response curve

4.15, which relates the magnitudes of the voltage and the current. By tuning the variable capacitor C, the frequency of the response peak may be adjusted to that desired. Providing the Q of the tuned circuit is appropriate (and as previously discussed, this will be influenced by the winding losses in the inductor) just one signal will then be within the *passband* of the tuned circuit, all other signals being relatively attenuated according to the circuit response. In other words, the circuit acts as a *bandpass filter*, passing signals within its passband, but rejecting those signals on either side. On the medium waveband, for example, each broadcast signal occupies a channel having about 10 kHz bandwidth, the channel centre frequencies being spaced by 10 kHz, and so the tuned circuit is required to select just one of these signals, while rejecting the remainder. The selected signal will then be passed on to circuits which detect or recover the music or speech modulation which is impressed onto the radio frequency carrier wave signal broadcast from the transmitter, and amplifying circuits then deliver this music or speech to the loudspeaker.

In the above application the tuned circuit is working as an *acceptor* of the required signal. In some cases, for example where a strong unwanted interference signal is present, the tuned circuit is used in the role of

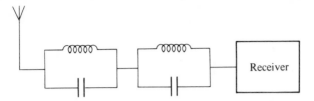

Fig. 4.16 Tuned circuit traps in an aerial connection to a receiver

rejector. Fig. 4.16 shows diagrammatically an aerial connected to a radio receiver. Two tuned circuit 'traps' have been inserted in series with the aerial. Providing these are high Q circuits, they will each present a very high dynamic impedance at the resonant frequency to which they are tuned—that is the two frequencies (in this case) which it is required to reject. This will prevent the two unwanted interfering signals from reaching the receiver input, while leaving all other signals relatively unaffected. Clearly similar results could be obtained by placing series tuned circuits in parallel with the receiver input.

Sinusoidal oscillators abound in electronics, being used in signal generators, radio and television receivers, and so on, and represent another application of tuned circuits. To understand how a tuned circuit may be used in an oscillator, consider the simple circuit shown in Fig. 4.17. We shall assume that by some means, energy has been introduced into this circuit, which has a perfect inductor and capacitor connected in parallel. According to the discussion in section 4.1, this energy will be shared in time varying proportions between the inductor and capacitor and will transfer from the capacitor to the inductor, and back again at a rate determined by the resonant frequency. The voltage across the tuned circuit, and the current through the components will therefore be varying sinusoidally at that frequency. However, since practically some resistance would be in series with the inductor, some of the energy stored in the reactive components would be lost during each sinusoidal cycle as the current passing through the resistor caused power to be dissipated. The total energy in the tuned circuit and the amplitude of the sinusoidal voltage

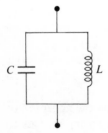

Fig. 4.17 Simple tuned circuit

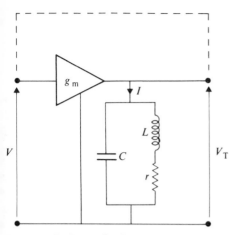

Fig. 4.18 Oscillator circuit

across it would therefore reduce to zero as time passed. This may be overcome by using the simple circuit shown in Fig. 4.18. Here a trans-conductance amplifier (VCCS) has its output connected to the tuned circuit. The amplifier delivers an output current I which is in phase with its input voltage V, and is given by $I = g_m V$, where g_m is known as the mutual conductance, or transconductance of the amplifier. If the amplifier were driven with a sinusoidal voltage at the resonant frequency of the tuned circuit, then a current at just the right frequency would be supplied to the tuned circuit which, by adjusting its amplitude, could supply the energy lost in the resistor r, and therefore maintain its required constant amplitude sinusoidal voltage developed across the tuned circuit. Now at resonance, the phasor voltage V_T developed across the tuned circuit is given by $V_T = \dfrac{L}{Cr} I$; that is, V_T and I are in phase, and so V_T and V are in phase. In fact

$$V_T = \frac{L}{Cr} g_m V \qquad (4.31)$$

The simplest way to derive the voltage V to drive the amplifier is simply to equate it to V_T by making the dotted connection shown in Fig. 4.18. Eq. (4.31) is then satisfied by setting $g_m = \dfrac{Cr}{L}$. Since the resonant frequency is the only frequency at which the tuned circuit is resistive, and has an impedance $\dfrac{L}{Cr}$, it is the only frequency at which Eq. (4.31) will be satisfied, and at which the circuit will oscillate. In practice, it is left to random electrical noise in the circuit to provide the initial energy in the tuned circuit. By designing g_m to be slightly greater than its theoretical value, the amplitude of voltage across the tuned circuit will rapidly build up until limited at the desired amplitude by circuits specially designed for that purpose. However, in simple terms, the circuit of Fig. 4.18 embodies the important concepts of all sinusoidal oscillators, of which there are many types.

The above discussion has dealt with just a few applications of tuned circuits. Although the examples given here mainly related to parallel circuits, similar applications exist for series tuned circuits, the choice depending, for example, on whether high or low dynamic impedances are required.

4.4 SUMMARY

This chapter has been concerned with an important class of electrical circuit. We have investigated the phenomenon of resonance in tuned circuits and have seen that when this occurs, the sinusoidal voltage and current at the terminals of the circuit are in phase, that is, the circuit appears resistive. As the frequency of an applied signal is varied, the circuit exhibits a frequency selective characteristic, both in terms of its amplitude and its phase response. The Q of the circuit is a measure of this selectivity, although we have seen that Q can also be related to the energy distribution in the circuit, or can be used as a measure of component quality factor, and in particular that of the circuit inductor. We shall see tuned circuit concepts being used further when a.c. power is discussed in Chapter 7.

Problems

1. A series tuned circuit comprises an inductor of value 1 mH, a 1 nF capacitor, and a resistor of value 10 Ω. Calculate the resonant frequency, dynamic impedance, Q, and the bandwidth of this circuit.
   (Answer: 10^6 rad/s, 10 Ω, 100, 10^4 rad/s)
2. A 100 mH inductor is connected in parallel with a 10 kΩ resistor and a capacitor of value 0.1 μF. The circuit is connected across a sinusoidal current source of amplitude 2 mA. If the frequency of the current source is the resonant frequency of the tuned circuit, find the amplitude of the current in the inductor.
   (Answer: 20 mA)
3. Design a series tuned circuit having a dynamic impedance of 100 Ω, resonant at 100 kHz with a bandwidth of 10 kHz.
   (Answer: $L = 1.59$ mH, $C = 1.59$ nF, $R = 100$ Ω)
4. A tuned circuit comprising a 10 mH inductor and a 10 nF capacitor connected in parallel is found to have a dynamic impedance of 100 kΩ. What is

the series resistance of the inductor? Calculate the Q of the circuit, and the frequencies at which the amplitude response has fallen by 3 dB from its maximum.

(Answer: 10 Ω, 100, 100.501 k rad/s, 99.501 k rad/s)

5. Find the resonant frequency, dynamic impedance, and the Q of the circuit shown in Fig. 4.19.

$$\left(\text{Answer: } \sqrt{\frac{CR^2 - L}{LC^2R^2}}, \frac{L}{CR}, \sqrt{\frac{CR^2 - L}{L}}\right)$$

6. Derive the resonant frequency and dynamic impedance for the circuit shown in Fig. 4.20.

$$\left(\text{Answer: } \frac{2}{(LC - C^2R^2)^{1/2}}, \frac{2LCR}{(LC + C^2R^2)}\right)$$

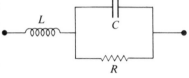

Fig. 4.19 Tuned circuit example for problem 5

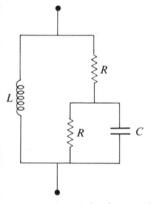

Fig. 4.20 Tuned circuit example for problem 6

5

CIRCUIT ANALYSIS TECHNIQUES

This chapter deals with techniques for circuit analysis from two points of view. In the following section, methods of circuit simplification will be discussed. As the name suggests, these methods ease the task of analysis by simplifying or reducing fairly complex circuits to an equivalent structure which is more manageable. Such simplification is possible in a wide range of circuit analysis problems, and the techniques are useful for by-hand analysis.

An alternative analysis technique which is attractive, particularly for computer implementation, is that of matrix analysis, and this will be considered in the rest of the chapter. In particular, we shall see that the systematic application of Kirchhoff's Current and Voltage Laws to a circuit gives rise to a matrix characterization of the circuit which may be written down by inspection. Simple manipulation of the matrix equation obtained then allows the unknown voltages and currents in the circuit to be determined, and completes the analysis.

5.1 CIRCUIT SIMPLIFICATION AND REDUCTION

Electronic circuits are frequently considered from a 'black box' viewpoint; that is one does not concern oneself with the detailed operation of the circuit, but rather tries to characterize the circuit simply by its behaviour at accessible terminals.

Fig. 5.1 shows a two terminal (or 'one-port') black box which might represent a power supply, signal generator, or possibly a transducer such as a record pick-up cartridge, and so on. In order that the effect of connecting this two terminal circuit to other circuits may be easily calculated, a simple equivalent circuit is sought. Such a circuit must reproduce the terminal properties of the black box—it must provide the same voltage and current at its terminals as the black box no matter what external circuit is connected to it. To find such an equivalent circuit, consider Fig. 5.2. Here a sinusoidal current source I, has been connected between the terminals of the black box. Any sources in the box are assumed to be operating at the same frequency, and this is also taken to be the frequency of the current source. As a special case, this may be a zero frequency, or d.c. source if all internal sources are themselves d.c. A voltage V is assumed to be developed across the terminals, and this voltage will now be determined. Invoking the principle of superposition, we may first set the current source to zero, and replace it by an open circuit as

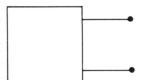

Fig. 5.1 Two terminal 'black box'

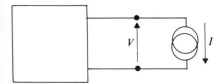

Fig. 5.2 Current source connected to the black box terminals

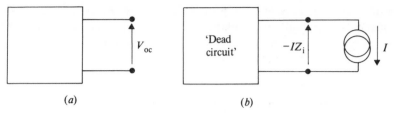

(a)   (b)

Fig. 5.3 Analysis of the black box configuration

shown in Fig. 5.3(a). If we had the configuration of the circuit in the black box, which may contain several voltage and current sources, each could now be considered in turn to determine the terminal voltage. This is seen to be the *open circuit voltage* V_{OC} of the black box, shown in Fig. 5.3(a). Next, the current source may be replaced, and all sources in the black box reduced to zero. This leaves a 'dead' circuit, consisting only of passive components which will have an impedance of, say, Z_i measured at the terminals. The current I flowing into this impedance will therefore develop a voltage $-IZ_i$ as shown in Fig. 5.3(b). Referring back to Fig. 5.2, the voltage V may therefore be expressed as

$$V = V_{OC} - IZ_i \tag{5.1}$$

Eq. (5.1) relates the terminal voltage V and current I for the black box in terms of two quantities V_{OC} and Z_i. It also suggests a very simple equivalent circuit for the black box, and this is shown in Fig. 5.4.

If an external current source is applied to this equivalent circuit in the manner previously considered, Eq. (5.1) again applies, indicating the equivalence. The circuit shown in Fig. 5.4 is known as a *Thévenin Equivalent Circuit*. The derivation of this circuit constitutes a proof for Thévenin's theorem, which in general terms states that 'any linear two terminal circuit consisting of sources and passive components may be represented by a voltage source, whose voltage is the open circuit voltage of the circuit, in series with an impedance which is that measured at the terminals of the circuit when all sources are reduced to zero'. Thévenin's original theorem was strictly concerned with d.c. sources and resistive components. However, the extension to sinusoidal sources is satisfactory

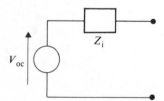

Fig. 5.4 Thévenin equivalent circuit for a two terminal black box

providing all sources have the same frequency, and that is the frequency at which the *internal* (or *output*) impedance Z_i is calculated or measured.

Example

Find the Thévenin equivalent for the circuit shown in Fig. 5.5.

Using the principle of superposition, the open circuit voltage V_{OC} is given by

$$V_{OC} = 18 \times \frac{(15 \times 10^3)}{(15 \times 10^3 + 30 \times 10^3)} + 10^{-3} \times \frac{(15 \times 10^3 \times 30 \times 10^3)}{(15 \times 10^3 + 30 \times 10^3)}$$

$$= 6 + 10 = 16 \text{ volts}$$

If the sources are reduced to zero, then the internal resistance R_i is given by the parallel combination of the two resistors, i.e., $R_i = \dfrac{(15 \times 10^3 \times 30 \times 10^3)}{(15 \times 10^3 + 30 \times 10^3)} = 10 \text{ k}\Omega$. The Thévenin equivalent circuit is therefore as shown in Fig. 5.6.

The structure of the Thévenin equivalent circuit was derived by connecting a current source between the terminals of the black box. Equally a voltage source could have been connected, as shown in Fig. 5.7. Using the

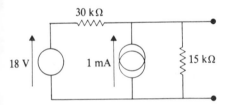

Fig. 5.5 Circuit example

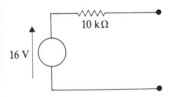

Fig. 5.6 Thévenin equivalent circuit for Fig. 5.5

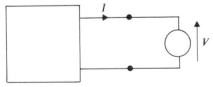

Fig. 5.7 Voltage source connected to the black box terminals

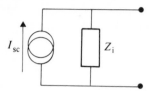

Fig. 5.8 Norton equivalent circuit for a two terminal black box

principle of superposition again, an expression for the current I may be obtained. Setting the external voltage source to zero will short circuit the terminals of the black box, and a short circuit current I_{SC} will flow. With all the sources in the black box reduced to zero a current $-V/Z_i$ will flow (in the direction of I) due to the external voltage source. The expression for I is therefore

$$I = I_{SC} - \frac{V}{Z_i} \tag{5.2}$$

This equation suggests a second simple equivalent circuit, known as the *Norton* equivalent, which is shown in Fig. 5.8.

The Norton and Thévenin circuits are alternative equivalents to the same black box, and are therefore equivalent to each other. If both equivalent circuits are left with their terminals open circuited, the same open circuit voltage V_{OC} must result. Referring to Fig. 5.4 and Fig. 5.8, this means

$$V_{OC} = I_{SC}Z_i \tag{5.3}$$

Again if both circuits have their terminals short circuited, the same current I_{SC} must flow, and referring again to the two figures, it will be seen that Eq. (5.3) again applies. In fact, Eq. (5.3) provides the link between the equivalent circuits, allowing one to be found from the other. In addition, Eq. (5.3) suggests an alternative method for the calculation or measurement of Z_i, namely $Z_i = \dfrac{V_{OC}}{I_{SC}}$.

Example

Find Norton and Thévenin equivalents for the circuit shown in Fig. 5.9 at a frequency of 10^3 rad/s.

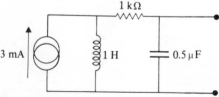

Fig. 5.9 Circuit example

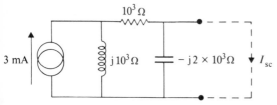

Fig. 5.10 Circuit of Fig. 5.9 with impedances annotated

At $\omega = 10^3$ rad/s, the inductor has an impedance of $j10^3 \times 1 = j10^3 \ \Omega$ while that of the capacitor is $-\dfrac{j1}{(10^3 \times 0.5 \times 10^{-6})} = -j2 \times 10^3 \ \Omega$. These values are inserted in Fig. 5.10. If the terminals are short circuited, the short circuit current I_{SC} is seen to be that flowing in the resistor. Using the current splitting rule

$$I_{SC} = 3 \times \frac{j10^3}{10^3 + j10^3} = \frac{j3}{1 + j1} = \frac{3}{2}(1 + j1) \text{ mA} \tag{5.4}$$

To find Z_i, the current source is reduced to zero, and the impedance seen from the terminals is calculated. This is:

$$Z_i = \frac{-j2 \times 10^3(10^3 + j10^3)}{10^3 + j10^3 - j2 \times 10^3} = -j2 \times 10^3 \frac{(1 + j1)}{(1 - j1)} = 2 \times 10^3 \ \Omega \tag{5.5}$$

Noting Fig. 5.8, the values for I_{SC} and Z_i may be incorporated into the Norton equivalent circuit shown in Fig. 5.11(a). Using Eq. (5.3), $V_{OC} = \dfrac{3}{2}(1 + j1) \text{ mA} \times 2 \text{ k}\Omega = 3(1 + j1) \text{ V}$, and so the Thévenin equivalent circuit may be drawn as Fig. 5.11(b). It will be noticed that at the frequency chosen, the output impedance Z_i is resistive in both these circuits. This is of course because the passive components in the circuit of Fig. 5.9 are at resonance at this frequency when viewed from the output terminals. At any other frequency the output impedance would have both a resistive and a reactive component. Also the Norton current source $I_{SC} = \dfrac{3}{2}(1 + j1) = \dfrac{3}{\sqrt{2}} \underline{/\pi/4} \text{ mA}$ has a magnitude and phase (relative to the original source in

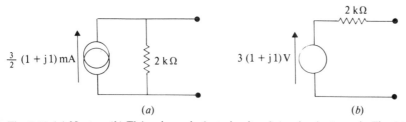

Fig. 5.11 (a) Norton, (b) Thévenin equivalent circuits of the circuit shown in Fig. 5.10

Fig. 5.9) which will vary with frequency, and clearly so does the Thévenin voltage source. It is important to remember therefore that a Norton or Thévenin equivalent circuit is only applicable at the frequency at which it is derived. Only in cases where, for example, all passive components in the original circuit are resistive, and the sources do not vary with frequency will a particular Norton or Thévenin equivalent circuit apply at all frequencies.

The Thévenin and Norton circuits which have been derived are equivalent to the original circuit only as far as their terminal behaviour is concerned. There is no equivalence within the circuits. For example, the power dissipation under open circuit conditions will be zero for the Thévenin equivalent, and finite for the Norton equivalent. Under short circuit, these conditions are interchanged. Clearly therefore it is not appropriate to use equivalent circuits as the basis for the calculation of power dissipated within the original black box circuit.

Consider the circuit shown in Fig. 5.12. If we seek the Thévenin equivalent of this circuit, then the open circuit voltage V_{OC} is required. At first sight, this does not seem to be simply obtainable. However, some progress can be made if we concentrate on the *star* or T circuit comprising the impedances Z_1, Z_2 and Z_3, and this is reproduced in Fig. 5.13(a). Identifying terminals or *nodes* ⓘ ⓙ and ⓚ as shown, an alternative structure shown in Fig. 5.13(b) will be derived which is equivalent to the star circuit. This equivalent is often described as a *delta* or π circuit. If the two circuits of Fig. 5.13 are to be equivalent, then the same impedance must be measured between any two of the nodes ⓘ, ⓙ and ⓚ in each circuit. By inspection, we may write:

$$\text{ⓘ–ⓚ}: \quad Z_1 + Z_2 = \frac{Z_B(Z_A + Z_C)}{Z_A + Z_B + Z_C} \tag{5.6}$$

$$\text{ⓘ–ⓙ}: \quad Z_1 + Z_3 = \frac{Z_A(Z_B + Z_C)}{Z_A + Z_B + Z_C} \tag{5.7}$$

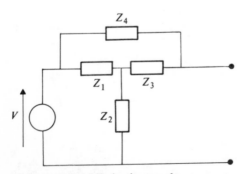

Fig. 5.12 Bridged-T circuit example

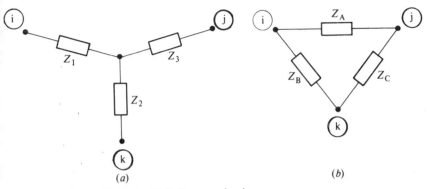

Fig. 5.13 (*a*) Star or T circuit, (*b*) Delta or π circuit

$$\text{(j)}-\text{(k)}: \quad Z_2 + Z_3 = \frac{Z_C(Z_A + Z_b)}{Z_A + Z_B + Z_C} \tag{5.8}$$

Eqs. (5.6)–(5.8) may now be solved for Z_A, Z_B and Z_C in terms of Z_1, Z_2 and Z_3, and vice versa. The results, which are obtained by simple algebra, are summarized in Table 5.1. The relationships in the first column constitute the delta-star (or π-T) transform, while those in the second column give the star-delta (or T-π) transform. It is not necessary to remember each relationship in detail, since a little consideration of the star and delta

Table 5.1

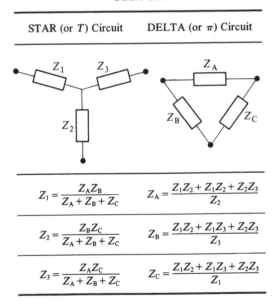

STAR (or T) Circuit	DELTA (or π) Circuit
$Z_1 = \dfrac{Z_A Z_B}{Z_A + Z_B + Z_C}$	$Z_A = \dfrac{Z_1 Z_2 + Z_1 Z_2 + Z_2 Z_3}{Z_2}$
$Z_2 = \dfrac{Z_B Z_C}{Z_A + Z_B + Z_C}$	$Z_B = \dfrac{Z_1 Z_2 + Z_1 Z_3 + Z_2 Z_3}{Z_3}$
$Z_3 = \dfrac{Z_A Z_C}{Z_A + Z_B + Z_C}$	$Z_C = \dfrac{Z_1 Z_2 + Z_1 Z_3 + Z_2 Z_3}{Z_1}$

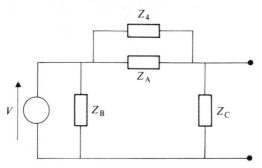

Fig. 5.14 The circuit of Fig. 5.12, with the star-delta transformation performed

circuits shows that:

$$Z_{\text{star}} = \frac{\text{product of the delta impedances connected to the same node}}{\text{sum of the delta impedances}}$$

$$(5.9)$$

$$Z_{\text{delta}} = \frac{\text{sum of the products of the star impedances taken two at a time}}{\text{opposite star impedance}}$$

$$(5.10)$$

Returning to the circuit of Fig. 5.12, this may now be redrawn as Fig. 5.14. (Note that here the T circuit Z_1–Z_2–Z_3 has been replaced by the π-circuit $Z_A - Z_B - Z_C$, which stresses this alternative terminology.) The open circuit voltage is now readily calculated as:

$$V_{\text{OC}} = V \frac{Z_C}{Z_C + Z_4 Z_A/(Z_4 + Z_A)} = V \frac{Z_C(Z_4 + Z_A)}{Z_C(Z_4 + Z_A) + Z_4 Z_A}$$

Substituting from Table 5.1; or using Eq. (5.10)

$$V_{\text{OC}} = \frac{V \dfrac{(Z_1 Z_2 + Z_1 Z_3 + Z_2 Z_3)}{Z_1} \left\{ Z_4 + \dfrac{(Z_1 Z_2 + Z_1 Z_3 + Z_2 Z_3)}{Z_2} \right\}}{\dfrac{(Z_1 Z_2 + Z_1 Z_3 + Z_2 Z_3)}{Z_1} \left\{ Z_4 + \dfrac{(Z_1 Z_2 + Z_1 Z_3 + Z_2 Z_3)}{Z_2} \right\} + Z_4 \dfrac{(Z_1 Z_2 + Z_1 Z_3 + Z_2 Z_3)}{Z_2}}$$

Cancelling the common factor $(Z_1 Z_2 + Z_1 Z_3 + Z_2 Z_3)$ and simplifying, this becomes:

$$V_{\text{OC}} = \frac{V(Z_1 Z_2 + Z_1 Z_3 + Z_2 Z_3 + Z_2 Z_4)}{(Z_1 Z_2 + Z_1 Z_4 + Z_1 Z_3 + Z_2 Z_3 + Z_2 Z_4)}$$

Example

Find the open circuit output voltage V_{OC} for the circuit shown in Fig. 5.15.

In this case we shall find it convenient to convert the delta circuit consisting of the inductor and two resistors into an equivalent star circuit,

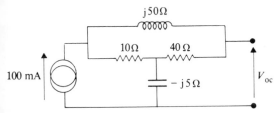

Fig. 5.15 Circuit example

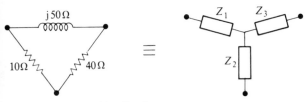

Fig. 5.16 Delta-star identification

according to Fig. 5.16. The sum of the delta impedances is

$10 + 40 + j50 = 50(1 + j1)$, and so using Eq. (5.9):

$$Z_1 = \frac{10 \times j50}{50(1 + j1)} = 5(1 + j1)\Omega$$

$$Z_2 = \frac{10 \times 40}{50(1 + j1)} = 4(1 - j1)\Omega$$

$$Z_3 = \frac{40 \times j50}{50(1 + j1)} = 20(1 + j1)\Omega$$

Fig. 5.15 may now be redrawn as Fig. 5.17. Since no current will flow through $Z_3 = 20(1 + j1)\Omega$, V_{OC} will be the voltage developed across the composite impedance $4(1 - j1) - j5 = 4 - j9\Omega$. Thus

$$V_{OC} = 0.1(4 - j9) = 0.4 - j0.9 \text{ volts.}$$

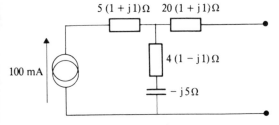

Fig. 5.17 Equivalent circuit for Fig. 5.15

The techniques discussed above are applicable in many circuit problems. However, with complex circuits, a more formal basis for circuit analysis is often required to minimize the computational effort. Such a formal approach is particularly attractive for computer implementation, where a logical algorithmic method for circuit analysis must be provided. Two such methods will now be introduced. These methods, which are based on the application of Kirchhoff's Law to the circuit undergoing analysis will be shown to give rise to matrix characterisations of the circuit. The simple manipulation of the matrix equations obtained then effects the circuit analysis.

5.2   NODAL ANALYSIS

Fig. 5.18 shows a general passive circuit in which we have concentrated our attention on one *node*. In this context, a node is an unique junction of circuit components—it may be thought of as a single soldered connection of all the components which are required to be connected together. In this case we are interested in the k-th node, assuming all n nodes in the circuit are numbered. We shall assume two further points; first that a current I_k derived from some source external to the circuit is flowing into node k, and second that node k is connected to every other node via a component which may be represented by its admittance. Thus, if no such component exists, it may be assigned an admittance of zero without affecting this assumption.

Applying Kirchoff's Current Law to node k, we have by inspection of Fig. 5.18:

$$I_k = (V_k - V_1)Y_{k1} + (V_k - V_2)Y_{k2} + \cdots + (V_k - V_n)Y_{kn}$$

$$= V_k \sum_{\substack{i=1 \\ i \neq k}}^{n} Y_{ki} + \sum_{\substack{i=1 \\ i \neq k}}^{n} V_i(-Y_{ki}) \tag{5.11}$$

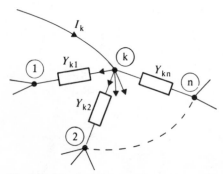

Fig. 5.18 Circuitry surrounding a single node in a general passive circuit

If we assign $y_{kk} = \sum\limits_{\substack{i=1 \\ i \neq k}}^{n} Y_{ki}$, and $y_{ki} = -Y_{ki}$ then Eq. (5.11) may be written as

$$I_k = \sum_{i=1}^{n} y_{ki} V_i \qquad (5.12)$$

If a similar equation is written for every other node, the equations may then be assembled into a matrix equation:

$$
\begin{bmatrix} I_1 \\ I_2 \\ \vdots \\ I_n \end{bmatrix}
=
\begin{bmatrix}
y_{11} & y_{12} & \cdots & y_{1n} \\
y_{21} & y_{22} & \cdots & y_{2n} \\
\vdots & \vdots & & \vdots \\
y_{n1} & y_{n2} & \cdots & y_{nn}
\end{bmatrix}
\begin{bmatrix} V_1 \\ V_2 \\ \vdots \\ V_n \end{bmatrix}
\qquad (5.13)
$$

where the square matrix is known as the *indefinite nodal admittance matrix*. From Eq. (5.12), it is seen that the formulation of this matrix is very straightforward, since

y_{kk} = the sum of all admittances connected to node k   (5.14)

y_{ki} = minus the (total) admittance connecting node k to node i   (5.15)

Note that $y_{ki} = y_{ik}$, and so we expect the matrix to be symmetric.

Example

Derive the nodal equations for the circuit shown in Fig. 5.19.

Fig. 5.19 is identical with the circuit of Fig. 5.15. However, in this case to facilitate the formulation of the nodal equations, the nodes of the circuit have been numbered, and the *admittances* of the components have been assigned. Noting Eq. (5.14) and Eq. (5.15), we may now proceed to the

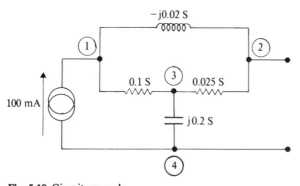

Fig. 5.19 Circuit example

nodal equations, which are:

$$\begin{bmatrix} I_1 \\ I_2 \\ I_3 \\ I_4 \end{bmatrix} = \begin{bmatrix} 10^{-1} \\ 0 \\ 0 \\ -10^{-1} \end{bmatrix} = \begin{bmatrix} 0.1 - j0.02 & j0.02 & -0.1 & 0 \\ j0.02 & 0.025 - j0.02 & -0.025 & 0 \\ -0.1 & -0.025 & 0.125 + j0.2 & -j0.2 \\ 0 & 0 & -j0.2 & j0.2 \end{bmatrix} \begin{bmatrix} V_1 \\ V_2 \\ V_3 \\ V_4 \end{bmatrix}$$

$$(5.16)$$

Note that the entries in the current vector corresponding to I_2 and I_3 are zero, since no external current is applied to nodes 2 and 3, and also that the matrix is symmetric as expected. This latter fact can clearly be exploited to speed up the formulation of the matrix.

It may be thought that the set of linear equations represented by Eq. (5.16) may now be solved for the unknown voltages V_1 to V_4.

However, this is not the case, since if we add the currents on the left hand side of Eq. (5.16), they sum to zero. Each of the columns on the right hand side of the equations also sums to zero. This arises because Kirchhoff's Current Law applies for the whole circuit; that is, the algebraic sum of currents entering a circuit is zero. In other words the set of equations expressed in Eq. (5.16) is *dependent*, since any equation can be expressed as a linear combination of the remainder. This is not only true for the circuit under consideration, but is generally true, and thus applies to Eq. (5.13). This problem may be overcome by striking out one of the equations in the set. However, this brings in another problem, since in the present case (Eq. (5.16)) for example, this will leave three equations in four unknowns (V_1 to V_4). This problem may be alleviated by noting that until now, the node voltages V_1 to V_4 have been assigned without reference to any datum. In most circuits, one node will usually be assigned as the *earth* or *ground* node, with potential zero volts, and all other voltages will be measured with respect to it. In other words, one of the voltages is not an unknown. In the present case, if node 4 is taken to be the ground node, then $V_4 = 0$. By deleting (for convenience) the current equation relating to node 4, Eq. (5.16) may therefore be reduced to:

$$\begin{bmatrix} I_1 \\ I_2 \\ I_3 \end{bmatrix} = \begin{bmatrix} 10^{-1} \\ 0 \\ 0 \end{bmatrix} = \begin{bmatrix} 0.1 - j0.02 & j0.02 & -0.1 \\ j0.02 & 0.025 - j0.02 & -0.025 \\ -0.1 & -0.025 & 0.125 + j0.2 \end{bmatrix} \begin{bmatrix} V_1 \\ V_2 \\ V_3 \end{bmatrix} \quad (5.17)$$

In the general case, if we assign node n as reference node, Eq. (5.13) becomes

$$\begin{bmatrix} I_1 \\ I_2 \\ \vdots \\ I_{n-1} \end{bmatrix} = \begin{bmatrix} y_{11} & y_{12} & \cdots & y_{1,n-1} \\ y_{21} & y_{22} & \cdots & y_{2,n-1} \\ \vdots & \vdots & & \vdots \\ y_{n-1,1} & y_{n-1,2} & \cdots & y_{n-1,n-1} \end{bmatrix} \begin{bmatrix} V_1 \\ V_2 \\ \vdots \\ V_{n-1} \end{bmatrix} \quad (5.18)$$

or

$$I = YV \qquad (5.19)$$

where Y is known as the *definite nodal admittance matrix*. For an n-node circuit, Y will have dimension $(n-1) \times (n-1)$, and is derived by using Eq. (5.14) and Eq. (5.15) for all nodes except ground.

Given a set of nodal equations in the form of Eq. (5.18), one of several well known methods such as Cramer's rule, Gaussian Elimination and so on may be chosen to obtain a solution for the unknown voltages. Indeed many sophisticated techniques exist which seek to minimize computational effort, maximize accuracy and minimize storage requirements for computer implementation. Such techniques, however, are outside the scope of this book. In cases where it is sensible to seek a solution by hand we may obtain the unknown voltages by pursuing the development of Eq. (5.18), and write Eq. (5.19) as

$$V = Y^{-1}I = ZI \qquad (5.20)$$

where Z is known as the nodal impedance matrix, and is the inverse of Y. Now the inverse of a matrix may be found by dividing its *adjoint* by its determinant, that is

$$Z = Y^{-1} = \frac{\text{adj } Y}{\text{det } Y} \qquad (5.21)$$

where the adjoint matrix is simply found by replacing each element y_{ij} of Y by its cofactor (that is, its signed minor) Δ_{ij}, and transposing the matrix which results. Thus, using Y as expressed in Eq. (5.18)

$$Z = \frac{1}{\text{det } Y}
\begin{bmatrix}
\Delta_{11} & \Delta_{21} & \cdots & \Delta_{n-1,1} \\
\Delta_{12} & \Delta_{22} & \cdots & \Delta_{n-1,2} \\
\vdots & \vdots & & \vdots \\
\Delta_{1,n-1} & \Delta_{2,n-1} & \cdots & \Delta_{n-1,n-1}
\end{bmatrix}
=
\begin{bmatrix}
Z_{11} & Z_{12} & \cdots & Z_{1,n-1} \\
Z_{21} & Z_{22} & \cdots & Z_{2,n-1} \\
\vdots & \vdots & & \vdots \\
Z_{n-1,1} & Z_{n-1,2} & \cdots & Z_{n-1,n-1}
\end{bmatrix}$$

$$(5.22)$$

We shall now assume that only one external current is applied to the circuit described by the general equation, Eq. (5.18); that is only one entry in the current vector I is non zero. (If this is not the case, then the principle of superposition may be invoked to transform the analysis into a series of analyses satisfying this assumption.) Without loss of generality we may take the current to be input to node 1. Writing Eq. (5.20) in full, we then have

$$\begin{bmatrix} V_1 \\ V_2 \\ \vdots \\ V_{n-1} \end{bmatrix}
=
\begin{bmatrix}
Z_{11} & Z_{12} & \cdots & Z_{1,n-1} \\
Z_{21} & Z_{22} & \cdots & Z_{2,n-1} \\
\vdots & \vdots & & \vdots \\
Z_{n-1,1} & Z_{n-1,2} & \cdots & Z_{n-1,n-1}
\end{bmatrix}
\begin{bmatrix} I_1 \\ 0 \\ \vdots \\ 0 \end{bmatrix}
=
\begin{bmatrix} Z_{11} \\ Z_{21} \\ \vdots \\ Z_{n-1,1} \end{bmatrix} I_1 \qquad (5.23)$$

Eq. (5.23) may now be used to find any of the unknown voltages in terms of I_1. Noting Eq. (5.22), we have

$$V_1 = Z_{11}I_1 = \frac{\Delta_{11}}{\det \mathbf{Y}} I_1$$

where Z_{11} is the *open circuit driving point impedance* between node 1 and ground. Also,

$$V_2 = Z_{21}I_1 = \frac{\Delta_{12}}{\det \mathbf{Y}} I_1$$

Here Z_{21} is the *open circuit transfer impedance* from node 1 to node 2, with input at node 1. Also, note that V_2, for example, can be expressed in terms of V_1

$$V_2 = \frac{Z_{21}}{Z_{11}} V_1 = \frac{\Delta_{12}}{\Delta_{11}} V_1$$

where $\left(\frac{Z_{21}}{Z_{11}}\right) = \left(\frac{\Delta_{12}}{\Delta_{11}}\right)$ is the *voltage transfer function* between node 1 and node 2, assuming an input to the circuit at node 1. In the general case, with the input connected to node k, a similar development to that above gives

$$\left. \begin{aligned} V_k = Z_{kk}I_k = \frac{\Delta_{kk}}{\det \mathbf{Y}} I_k. \quad V_j = Z_{jk}I_k = \frac{\Delta_{kj}}{\det \mathbf{Y}} I_k \\ V_j = \frac{\Delta_{kj}}{\Delta_{kk}} V_k \end{aligned} \right\} \tag{5.24}$$

Eqs. (5.24) therefore allow a wide range of circuit functions to be calculated in terms of the determinant and cofactors of the definite nodal admittance matrix $\mathbf{Y}$.

Returning to the circuit of Fig. 5.19 which was used as an example for the formulation of the nodal equations, Eq. (5.17) gives

$$\mathbf{Y} = \begin{bmatrix} 0.1 - j0.02 & j0.02 & -0.1 \\ j0.02 & 0.025 - j0.02 & -0.025 \\ -0.1 & -0.025 & 0.125 - j0.2 \end{bmatrix} \tag{5.25}$$

With the input at node 1, we may now find the voltage at node 2. From Eqs. (5.24)

$$V_2 = \frac{\Delta_{12}}{\det \mathbf{Y}} I_1$$

Using Eq. (5.25)

$$\Delta_{12} = - \begin{vmatrix} j0.02 & -0.025 \\ -0.1 & 0.125 + j0.2 \end{vmatrix} = - \{j0.02(0.125 + j0.2) - (-0.025)(-0.1)\}$$

$$= - (j0.0025 - 0.004 - 0.0025) = 6.5 \times 10^{-3} - j2.5 \times 10^{-3}$$

Det Y may be found by performing a Laplacian expansion along the first row of the matrix:

$$\det Y = (0.1 - j0.02)\Delta_{11} + (j0.02)\Delta_{12} + (-0.1)\Delta_{13} \qquad (5.26)$$

where

$$\Delta_{11} = \begin{vmatrix} 0.025 - j0.02 & -0.025 \\ -0.025 & 0.125 + j0.2 \end{vmatrix} = 6.5 \times 10^{-3} + j2.5 \times 10^{-3}$$

$$\Delta_{13} = \begin{vmatrix} j0.02 & 0.025 - j0.02 \\ -0.1 & -0.025 \end{vmatrix} = 2.5 \times 10^{-3} + j2.5 \times 10^{-3}$$

Substituting the three cofactors in Eq. (5.26):

$$\det Y = (0.1 - j0.02)(6.5 \times 10^{-3} + j2.5 \times 10^{-3}) + (j0.02)(6.5 \times 10^{-3} - j2.5 \times 10^{-3})$$
$$+ (-0.1)(2.5 \times 10^{-3} - j2.5 \times 10^{-3})$$
$$= 5 \times 10^{-4} + j5 \times 10^{-4}$$

$$\therefore \quad V_2 = \left[\frac{6.5 \times 10^{-3} - j2.5 \times 10^{-3}}{5 \times 10^{-4} + j5 \times 10^{-4}} \right] I_1 = (4 - j9)I_1$$

and with $I_1 = 100\,\text{mA}$, $V_2 = 0.4 - j0.9$ volts, thus confirming the result previously obtained.

Nodal analysis is particularly attractive since the definite nodal admittance matrix may be written down by inspection of the circuit in question, and the solution of the analysis—the node voltages—are quantities which are usually of interest to the engineer. The voltages can usually be readily measured in a practical circuit. An alternative analysis technique, based on Kirchhoff's Voltage Law, will be introduced in the next section. This technique, known as loop, or mesh analysis has one advantage over nodal analysis in that in some circumstances fewer equations are required to characterize a given circuit.

5.3 LOOP (MESH) ANALYSIS

Kirchhoff's Voltage Law states that the algebraic sum of the voltages around any closed path in a circuit is zero. Thus, by the appropriate choice of a sufficient number of closed paths, or loops, in a circuit, a set of Kirchhoff's Voltage Law equations may be assembled which characterize the circuit. For example, Fig. 5.20 shows a circuit in which two alternative choices of loops have been made. In each case *loop currents* have been identified, and have been assigned an arbitrary direction. In Fig. 5.20(a), the chosen loops coincide with the meshes of the circuit, where the term mesh is used by analogy with the mesh of a fisherman's net. In common usage, the words loop and mesh are often used interchangeably, although strictly the term mesh is only applicable to the collection of components which

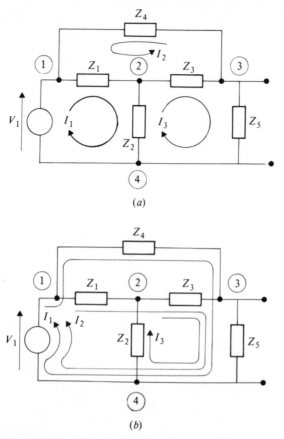

Fig. 5.20 Alternative choices of loops for the application of Kirchhoff's Voltage Law

bound a space in a circuit. This definition requires that the circuit be *planar*, that is that it can be drawn on a flat surface without crossovers of component connections.

Applying Kirchhoff's Voltage Law to the three meshes of Fig. 5.20(a), we have:

$$\text{mesh 1:} \quad V_1 = Z_1(I_1 + I_2) + Z_2(I_1 - I_3)$$

$$\text{mesh 2:} \quad 0 = Z_1(I_2 + I_1) + Z_4I_2 + Z_3(I_2 + I_3)$$

$$\text{mesh 3:} \quad 0 = Z_2(I_3 - I_1) + Z_3(I_3 + I_2) + Z_5I_3$$

Rearranging these equations, we may write

$$V_1 = (Z_1 + Z_2)I_1 + Z_1I_2 - Z_2I_3$$

$$0 = Z_1I_1 + (Z_1 + Z_3 + Z_4)I_2 + Z_3I_3$$

$$0 = -Z_2I_1 + Z_3I_2 + (Z_2 + Z_3 + Z_5)I_3$$

,.e.,

$$\begin{bmatrix} V_1 \\ 0 \\ 0 \end{bmatrix} = \begin{bmatrix} Z_1 + Z_2 & Z_1 & -Z_2 \\ Z_1 & Z_1 + Z_3 + Z_4 & Z_3 \\ -Z_2 & Z_3 & Z_2 + Z_3 + Z_5 \end{bmatrix} \begin{bmatrix} I_1 \\ I_2 \\ I_3 \end{bmatrix} \qquad (5.27)$$

or

$$V = ZI \qquad (5.28)$$

Here Z is known as the *loop impedance matrix*. It should not be confused with the node impedance matrix discussed in the last section. As Eq. (5.28) shows, Z relates the vector of loop currents I to the vector of voltage sources in each loop V. Inspection of Eq. (5.27) suggests a relatively straightforward way of formulating the loop impedance matrix Z which is generally applicable. Denoting the i-th diagonal entry of Z by z_{ii}, and the general off-diagonal entry by z_{ij}, we see that

$$z_{ii} = \text{(the sum of the impedances in the i-th loop)} \qquad (5.29)$$

$$z_{ij} = \sigma_{ij} \text{ (the sum of the impedances common to loop i and loop j)} \qquad (5.30)$$

where $\sigma_{ij} = +1\ (-1)$ if I_i and I_j flow in the same (opposite) direction through the common impedances. Thus the loop impedance matrix will be symmetric.

The formulation of the loop impedance matrix can therefore be carried out by inspection, once loop currents have been assigned. However, before accepting this as a general technique, one important question must be considered, namely, how many loop currents must be specified to adequately describe a circuit? This question may be answered by considering the number of nodes in a circuit. Imagine the nodes to be terminal posts, and that the circuit is to be constructed by soldering components to these terminals according to the circuit diagram. Then a little thought shows that the maximum number of components which can be so connected without forming a loop is $n - 1$ for an n node circuit. Such a collection of components is known as a *tree*, for obvious reasons. Fig. 5.21

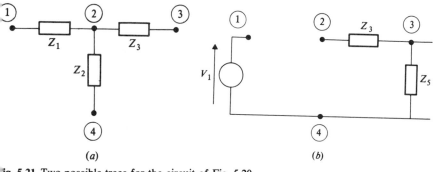

(a)   (b)

Fig. 5.21 Two possible trees for the circuit of Fig. 5.20

shows two of the several possible trees for the circuit of Fig. 5.20. In this case, there are $4 - 1 = 3$ components in each tree. By definition, if there are a total of b components to be connected in the circuit (including sources), then each of the remaining $b - (n - 1) = b - n + 1$ components will produce a loop when individually connected in circuit. Furthermore, each of the loop equations which may be then written will be independent of the others, since it will contain a term relating to the impedance of the component completing the loop, and this term will be absent from the other equations. To summarize, $b - n + 1$ independent loops may be formed for a circuit with b components (including sources) and n nodes. Having selected some tree for a circuit, these loops may be identified, and an arbitrary loop current direction may be assigned for each one. Eq. (5.29) and Eq. (5.30) may then be used to formulate Z, and the voltage vector V may be determined by assigning its i-th element as the algebraic sum of the voltage sources in the i-th loop. In the present example, the reader may care to check that the loops identified in Fig. 5.20(a) and Fig. 5.20(b) correspond to the trees depicted in Fig. 5.21(a) and Fig. 5.21(b) respectively.

In general therefore, we have uncovered by example a method of deriving the loop equations, which may be written in the form given in Eq. (5.28). To complete the analysis, these equations may now be solved as

$$I = Z^{-1}V = YV \qquad (5.31)$$

where Y is the *loop admittance matrix* (not to be confused with the nodal matrix dealt with previously) and its elements are known as *short circuit admittances*. Y may be obtained from Z by dividing adj Z by det Z in the usual way. If there is only one voltage source in a circuit, and further the selected tree used to form Z does not include that source, then only one equation incorporating the source voltage will result in the loop equations. This simplifies Eq. (5.31), since if for example the source is associated with loop 1, then Eq. (5.31) becomes, with $m = b - n + 1$

$$\begin{bmatrix} I_1 \\ I_2 \\ \vdots \\ I_m \end{bmatrix} = \frac{1}{\det Z} \begin{bmatrix} \Delta_{11} & \Delta_{21} & \cdots & \Delta_{m1} \\ \Delta_{12} & \Delta_{22} & \cdots & \Delta_{m2} \\ \vdots & \vdots & & \vdots \\ \Delta_{1m} & \Delta_{2m} & \cdots & \Delta_{mm} \end{bmatrix} \begin{bmatrix} V_1 \\ 0 \\ \vdots \\ 0 \end{bmatrix} = \frac{1}{\det Z} \begin{bmatrix} \Delta_{11} \\ \Delta_{12} \\ \vdots \\ \Delta_{1m} \end{bmatrix} V_1$$

Thus, $I_1 = y_{11}V_1 = \dfrac{\Delta_{11}}{\det Z} V_1$, $I_2 = y_{21}V_1 = \dfrac{\Delta_{12}}{\det Z} V_1$ and so on.

In the general case, where the voltage source is present in the k-th loop, we have

$$I_k = y_{kk}V_k = \frac{\Delta_{kk}}{\det Z} V_k; \quad I_j = y_{jk}V_k = \frac{\Delta_{kj}}{\det Z} V_k \qquad (5.32)$$

Example

Find the voltage V in the bridge circuit shown in Fig. 5.22.

To analyse this circuit using the loop method, we begin by selecting a

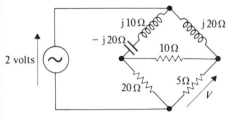

Fig. 5.22 Bridge circuit

tree. There are $n = 5$ nodes in this circuit, and so $5 - 1 = 4$ components will be in the tree. The tree shown in Fig. 5.23(a) will be satisfactory for our purposes. The total number of components $b = 7$, and so $b - n + 1 = 7 - 5 + 1 = 3$ loop equations will result in this problem. Inserting the three remaining components, loop currents may be assigned in the arbitrary directions shown in Fig. 5.23(b). Noting Eq. (5.29), Eq. (5.30), and the impedance values shown in Fig. 5.22, we may now write down the loop equations:

$$\begin{bmatrix} 2 \\ 0 \\ 0 \end{bmatrix} = \begin{bmatrix} 20 - j10 & -20 & j10 \\ -20 & 35 & -10 \\ j10 & -10 & 10 + j10 \end{bmatrix} \begin{bmatrix} I_1 \\ I_2 \\ I_3 \end{bmatrix}$$

Using Eq. (5.32), we may find I_2 as

$$I_2 = \frac{\Delta_{12}}{\det Z} \cdot 2 \qquad (5.33)$$

where

$$\Delta_{12} = - \begin{vmatrix} -20 & -10 \\ j10 & 10 + j10 \end{vmatrix} = -\{(-20)(10 + j10) - (-10)(j10)\} = 200 + j100$$

Also, expanding along the first row of Z

$$\det Z = (20 - j10)\Delta_{11} - 20\Delta_{12} + j10\Delta_{13}$$

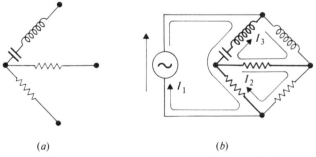

(a)   (b)

Fig. 5.23 (a) tree, (b) loop assignments for the circuit of Fig. 5.22

where

$$\Delta_{11} = \begin{vmatrix} 35 & -10 \\ -10 & 10 + j10 \end{vmatrix} = (35)(10 + j10) - (-10)(-10) = 250 + j350$$

and

$$\Delta_{13} = \begin{vmatrix} -20 & 35 \\ j10 & -10 \end{vmatrix} = (-20)(-10) - (35)(j10) = 200 - j350$$

Thus

$$\det Z = (20 - j10)(250 + j350) - 20(200 + j100) + j10(200 - j350)$$
$$= 8.0 \times 10^3 + j4.5 \times 10^3$$

Substituting into Eq. (5.33)

$$I_2 = \frac{200 + j100}{8.0 \times 10^3 + j4.5 \times 10^3} \cdot 2$$

Finally, we note that $V = 5I_2$, and so

$$V = \frac{2 \times 10^3 + j10^3}{8.0 \times 10^3 + j4.5 \times 10^3} = 0.243 - j0.012 \text{ volts}$$

It will be noted that a nodal analysis of the same circuit would require $n - 1 = 4$ equations. In other words, the nodal admittance matrix would have dimension 4×4, while the loop matrix is 3×3. We see here the major advantage of the loop method—that in certain cases (when $b - n + 1 < n - 1$), fewer equations are required than with the nodal method, leading to less computational effort.

5.4 SUMMARY

The Thévenin and Norton equivalent circuits discussed in this chapter lie at the heart of circuit analysis. We have seen that a linear circuit of any complexity, when considered as a two terminal black box, can be modelled by an equivalent circuit consisting of only two components. Subsequent analysis of circuits connected to such a black box is then much simplified, and this aspect will be given further consideration in Chapter 6 and Chapter 7. These two equivalent circuits thus provide circuit simplification. Another simplification technique which has been discussed is based on the star-delta transformation which accomplishes a transformation of the topology or structure of a circuit. The application of this technique in a complex circuit is limited only by the ingenuity of the engineer. On the other hand the techniques of nodal and loop analysis provide more formal methods of circuit analysis which is conducted according to a well defined set of rules. Although these techniques can lead to numerical complexity, ey are logical approaches, and so are particularly suitable for computer nplementation. As we have seen, the nodal method is a little more traightforward than the loop method, and notwithstanding the fact that in ertain circumstances fewer loop equations are required than nodal equaons for a particular circuit problem, it is nodal analysis which has found vour amongst electronic engineers.

'roblems

. Find Thévenin and Norton equivalent circuits for the circuit shown in Fig. 5.24.

$$\left(\text{Answer: } V_{OC} = 1.5 \text{ V, } R = 750 \text{ }\Omega; \ I_{sc} = \frac{8}{3} \text{ mA, } R = 750 \text{ }\Omega\right)$$

. Derive the Norton equivalent for the circuit shown in Fig. 5.25 at a frequency $\omega = 10^6$ rad/s.

(Answer: $I_{sc} = 2\sqrt{2}$ mA $/45°$ in parallel with an impedance $0.707(1 - j1)$ kΩ)

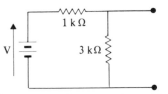

ig. **5.24** Circuit example for problem 1

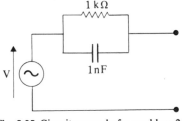

ig. **5.25** Circuit example for problem 2

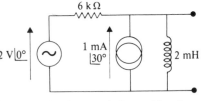

Fig. **5.26** Circuit example for problem 3

3. Find a Thévenin equivalent circuit for the circuit shown in Fig. 5.26 and hence calculate the current which would flow in a 400 Ω resistor connected to the terminals of the circuit. Assume a frequency of 10^6 rad/s.
   (Answer: $V_{OC} = 2.47$ V $\underline{/94.2°}$ in series with an impedance of $(0.6 + j1.8)$ kΩ 1.2 mA $\underline{/33.3°}$)

4. Using the delta/star transformation, find the resistance between the nodes A and B in Fig. 5.27.
   (Answer: 1.87 kΩ)

5. Find the conditions under which the two circuits shown in Fig. 5.28(a) and (b) are equivalent.
   (Answer: $C_a = CR_2/(R_1 + R_2)$, $C_b = CR_1/(R_1 + R_2)$, $R_a = R_1$, $R_b = R_2$, $L = CR_1R_2$, $R_c = R_1 + R_2$)

6. Use nodal analysis to find the amplitude and phase of the voltage V_2 in Fig. 5.29 with reference to an input voltage V_1 at a frequency 10^6 rad/s.

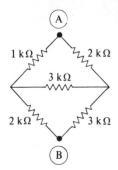

Fig. 5.27 Resistive bridge circuit (problem 4)

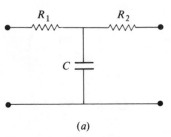

(a)

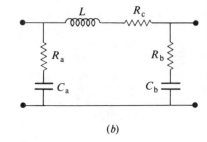

(b)

Fig. 5.28 Circuit equivalents (problem 5)

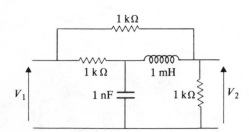

Fig. 5.29 Circuit example for problem 6

$$\left(\text{Answer: } \frac{|V_2|}{|V_1|} = 0.45, \ \phi = -26.6°\right)$$

The Twin-T circuit shown in Fig. 5.30 has a 'notch' characteristic; that is, at some frequency the output voltage V_0 is zero. Use nodal analysis to find the frequency.

$$\left(\text{Answer: } \omega = \frac{1}{CR} \text{ rad/s}\right)$$

Using the loop analysis method, calculate the magnitude and phase of the output voltage V_0 in the circuit of Fig. 5.31 with reference to the input voltage V_{in} at a frequency of 250 rad/s.

$$\left(\text{Answer: } \frac{|V_o|}{|V_{in}|} = 0.4, \ \phi = 0°\right)$$

Show, using loop analysis, that the impedance which the circuit shown in Fig. 5.32 offers to the voltage source V_{in} is independent of frequency, and find the value of this impedance.
(Answer: 10 kΩ)

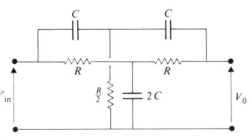

Fig. 5.30 Twin-T circuit (problem 7)

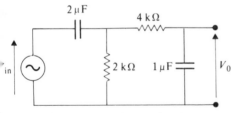

Fig. 5.31 Circuit example for problem 8

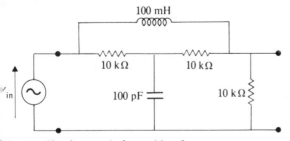

Fig. 5.32 Circuit example for problem 9

6

NONLINEAR CIRCUIT COMPONENTS

The topics of the previous chapters were all based on an assumption of linearity in the circuit components. In practice, of course, no component is truly linear, although in many cases it is a satisfactory engineering approximation to assume linearity. However, some electronic components have such grossly nonlinear voltage–current relationships that no such assumption can be justified. Semiconductor diodes and transistors are familiar examples of such components, although many others exist including thermistors, voltage dependent capacitors, saturating inductors and so on. Since the components are not linear, the techniques which we have considered in previous chapters are not appropriate. Indeed, in the most general case, circuits incorporating nonlinear components together with near capacitors, inductors and resistors require the solution of nonlinear differential equations for their analysis. Frequently, no analytic solution to such equations exist, and only numerical values can be obtained for the solution after a not inconsiderable computational effort.

In this chapter, we shall investigate simple nonlinear circuits and seek methods for their analysis. In particular, we shall find that providing an approximate solution to the analysis is acceptable (although in fact solutions are often to a good degree of accuracy), circuits incorporating nonlinear components may be *linearised*, and the techniques of linear analysis may then be invoked.

.1   NONLINEAR CIRCUIT ANALYSIS

Fig. 6.1 shows the symbol for a semiconductor diode to which voltage and current directions have been appended. (In this chapter we shall use upper case letters to represent d.c. voltages and currents, and lower case letters will presently be used to indicate small variations about these voltages and currents.) The characteristics of the diode are such that with a positive voltage applied in the direction shown, a substantial current can flow, while the voltage direction is reversed, only a small *leakage* current will flow. Under these conditions, the diode is said to be *forward biased* and *reverse biased* respectively. A graph of a typical silicon diode characteristic is shown in Fig. 6.2. It may be shown that the semiconductor diode may be characterized by the diode equation, which is usually taken to be

$$I = I_s(e^{qV/kT} - 1) \qquad (6.1)$$

Here, q is the charge on the electron, k is Boltzman's constant and T represents absolute temperature. For an operating temperature of around $0°C$, $\dfrac{kT}{q}$ is usually taken to be $25\,\text{mV}$. I_s is known as the saturation or leakage current, and typically has values of the order of $10^{-14}\,\text{A}$.

Fig. 6.3 shows a simple circuit in which the diode is forward biased into conduction by the application of a battery of voltage E. The current I is limited by the resistor R. The problem is to find V and I, given E and R. Clearly, whatever current I flows in this circuit, it must be related to the voltage V according to Eq. (6.1). In other words, the solution to the problem must be represented by a point on the diode characteristic shown

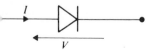

Fig. 6.1 Diode symbol

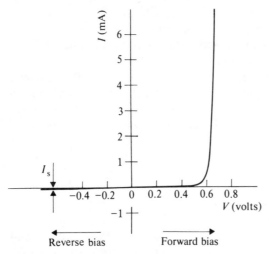

Fig. 6.2 Silicon diode characteristic

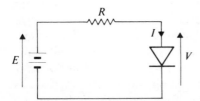

Fig. 6.3 Simple diode resistor circuit

in Fig. 6.2. To find this point, we may turn to consider the resistor in Fig. 6.3. By Ohm's Law,

$$I = \frac{E - V}{R} = -\frac{1}{R} \cdot V + \frac{E}{R} \tag{6.2}$$

Eq. (6.2) is the equation of a straight line which has slope $-\frac{1}{R}$, and intercepts with the current and voltage axis at $\frac{E}{R}$ and E respectively. Again, the solution to the problem at hand must be represented by a point on this straight line. Fig. 6.4 shows the diode and the resistor characteristics superimposed, and it is evident that the solution is given by the intersection of these two graphs. The solution to the problem is the current I_Q and voltage V_Q associated with the diode. These quantities are sometimes known as the *quiescent* values of current and voltage, that is the values of current and voltage established by the d.c. source applied to the diode–resistor circuit.

This simple graphical approach gives us one means of analysing the simple circuit load consideration. The straight line representing Eq. (6.2)

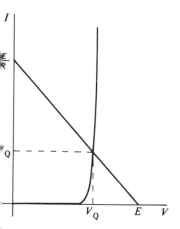

ig. 6.4 Load line solution of the diode resistor circuit

s known as a *load–line*, and the intersection of the load line with the
ionlinear characteristic gives us the solution we seek. This technique is
ipplicable in a wide variety of problems, but since it necessitates drawing
graphs, it is at best tedious and time consuming.

An alternative approach is to recognize that Eq. (6.1) and Eq. (6.2)
epresent two simultaneous equations in I and V. Thus, using Eq. (6.2), I
nay be eliminated in Eq. (6.1) to give

$$\frac{E - V}{R} = I_s[e^{qV/kT} - 1]$$

.e.,

$$I_s[e^{qV/kT} - 1] - \frac{(E - V)}{R} = 0 \tag{6.3}$$

Since in a particular problem, only V will be unknown in Eq. (6.3), we
night now seek to solve Eq. (6.3) for V in terms of the known quantities. A
quick consideration of Eq. (6.3), however, leads to the sobering conclusion
hat there is no analytic solution for V in this equation. In other words, V
:annot be expressed as a combination of known and tabulated functions
log, tan, exp, etc.) of the known quantities. Thus, despite the simplicity of
he circuit of Fig. 6.3, and the associated equations, no expression for V
:an be found.

In fact, the only way to solve Eq. (6.3) is by *iteration*, that is by guessing
he value of V which may satisfy the equation, and then successively
mproving the guess. For example, Eq. (6.3) may be rewritten as $f(V) = 0$,
vhere $f(V)$ is the nonlinear function of V on the left hand side of Eq. (6.3).
f we guess that $V = V_1$ may satisfy Eq. (6.3), then it is unlikely that the
;uess will be exactly correct. That being the case, a correction ΔV is

sought such that

$$f(V_1 + \Delta V) = 0 \qquad (6.4$$

An approximate value for this correction may be obtained by firs^t expanding Eq. (6.4) as a Taylor Series, that is:

$$f(V_1 + \Delta V) = f(V_1) + \frac{\Delta V}{1!}f'(V_1) + \frac{(\Delta V)^2}{2!}f''(V_1) + \frac{(\Delta V)^3}{3!}f'''(V_1) + \cdots$$

$$(6.5$$

Here, the primes denote differentiation with respect of V. Now if V_1 is a good guess, that is ΔV is small, then $(\Delta V)^2$, $(\Delta V)^3$ and so on may be ignored. Eq. (6.5) then becomes

$$f(V_1 + \Delta V) = f(V_1) + \Delta V f'(V_1) = 0$$

i.e.,

$$\Delta V = \frac{-f(V_1)}{f'(V_1)}$$

An improved version of the initial guess is therefore given by

$$V_2 = V_1 + \Delta V$$

i.e.,

$$V_2 = V_1 - \frac{f(V_1)}{f'(V_1)} \qquad (6.6$$

Of course, the values given by Eq. (6.6) are unlikely to be exactly correct since an approximation was introduced by truncating the Taylor Series o: Eq. (6.5). Further improvement may therefore be obtained by repeating th_e process to obtain better guesses V_3, then V_4 and so on. Generalising Eq (6.6), we have in the general case

$$V_{n+1} = V_n - \frac{f(V_n)}{f'(V_n)} \qquad (6.7$$

Here V_{n+1} is the $(n + 1)$th approximant to the solution of the origina_l equation $f(V) = 0$. Clearly, if for some n, $f(V_n) = 0$ in Eq. (6.7), then V_n is the exact solution, and $V_{n+1} = V_n$. Thus, if two successive values V_{n+1} and V_n are the same, then the solution has been found. It is rare that such an exact solution will be found in practice, and usually the solution is accepted if successive values are coincident to a given number of decima_l places.

Example

The diode shown in Fig. 6.5 has a saturation current $I_s = 10^{-14}$ A. Determine the quiescent diode voltage and current.

g. 6.5 Circuit example

Referring to Eq. (6.3), and substituting values leads to

$$f(V) = 10^{-14}(e^{40V} - 1) - \frac{(10 - V)}{4.7 \times 10^3}$$

d so

$$f'(V) = 40 \times 10^{-14}e^{40V} + \frac{1}{4.7 \times 10^3}$$

q. (6.7) then becomes

$$V_{n+1} = V_n - \frac{\left[10^{-14}(e^{40V_n} - 1) - \frac{(10 - V_n)}{4.7 \times 10^3}\right]}{\left[40 \times 10^{-14}e^{40V_n} + \frac{1}{4.7 \times 10^3}\right]} \tag{6.8}$$

For reasons which will presently become clear, an initial guess $V_1 = 0.7$ lts will be taken. Substituting this into the right hand side of Eq. (6.8), V_2 ay be found, and so on. Working to three decimal places, the results of ese calculations are shown in Table 6.1.

Table 6.1

V_1	0.7
V_2	0.678
V_3	0.661
V_4	0.653
V_5	0.650
V_6	0.650

To three decimal places, the technique converges to the solution in five rations, giving $V_Q = 0.65$ volts, whence $I_Q = \frac{(10 - 0.65)}{4.7 \times 10^3} = 1.989$ mA.

This iterative technique for determining the solution of nonlinear equa- ns is known as Newton's method. This technique is said to be *quadra- ally convergent*, which means in essence that providing the method is nverging, the number of correct significant figures in the solution roughly doubles at each iteration. Sometimes, either through the selection of a ba‹ initial guess, or because the character of the function under consideratio‹ introduces numerical instability into the iterative process, Newton' method may not converge. This is usually evident from the erratic value‹ of the intermediate results as the iterations proceed. In such cases on‹ must either use a more sophisticated technique than the simple metho‹ discussed above, or select a different initial guess, and restart the proces‹

While Newton's method provides a means by which nonlinear equation‹ may be solved to give a result (in this case the diode voltage) with som‹ apparent precision, such precision is not always required in the day to da‹ work of the electronics engineer. There are two main reasons for thi‹ First, the manufacturing spreads, or tolerances of electronic component‹ mean that it is seldom that the precise characteristics of a component wi‹ be known, and thus attempts to provide a mathematical description c‹ their behaviour will be prone to error. Secondly, it is because of th‹ uncertainty in the precise component characteristics that modern circu‹ design utilises feedback techniques. Such techniques (which are outside th‹ scope of this book) serve to minimize the effects which small deviations c‹ component have on the performance of a circuit. Thus, in many cases, it ‹ neither necessary or possible to determine the precise characteristics c‹ quiescent points of practical linear or nonlinear components.

With this in mind we may return to the circuit of Fig. 6.3, and the grap‹ shown in Fig. 6.4. If two further load lines are drawn, for d.c. voltage‹ $E_1 > E$ and $E_2 < E$ respectively, new quiescent points are established ‹ shown in Fig. 6.6. It will be seen that the three quiescent voltages (obtaine‹ by projecting the intersection of each load line with the diode characterist‹ onto the voltage axis) are of roughly the same value. This is because eac‹ such intersection occurs on the steep part of the diode characteristic. ‹

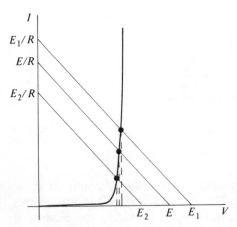

Fig. 6.6 Variation of quiescent point with varying d.c. input voltage

fact, consideration of Eq. (6.1) shows that an increase of only 60 mV in the diode voltage will lead to an approximately ten-fold increase in diode current, which indicates the steepness of the characteristic. Alternatively we may say that currents in the range from μA to mA may be established in a silicon diode for voltages in the range of 0.5 to 0.7 volts. For this reason, we can assume that with d.c. currents of the order of milliamps flowing through a diode, then as a rule of thumb the diode voltage will be around 0.6–0.7 volts. This rule of thumb, which has become standard in electronics, led to the initial guess of 0.7 volts in the example of Newton's method given above.

To sum up, while there will occasionally be circuit problems requiring a precise computation of the quiescent conditions of a diode circuit, in many cases the nonlinear characteristic may be ignored, and a voltage selected from the typical range may be assumed for the voltage drop across the diode, thus simplifying the analysis.

Similar observations may be made with regard to the bipolar transistor, which will be discussed later in this chapter. Other nonlinear components must be considered in their own light, and in cases where a rule of thumb is not appropriate, then recourse must be made to the graphical approach, or to the use of Newton's method.

Example

In the circuit shown in Fig. 6.7, N represents a nonlinear resistor which has a terminal characteristic $I = 10^{-3} V^3$ amperes. Determine the quiescent output voltage of this circuit.

Kirchhoff's Current Law requires that

$$\frac{6 - V}{2 \times 10^3} = I + \frac{V}{2 \times 10^3} = 10^{-3} V^3 + \frac{V}{2 \times 10^3}$$

.e.,

$$10^{-3} V^3 + 10^{-3} V - 3 \times 10^{-3} = 0$$

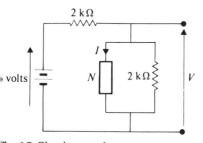

Fig. 6.7 Circuit example

or

$$f(V) = V^3 + V - 3 = 0 \tag{6.9}$$

In this case, while the nonlinear component has a cubic characteristic, it is not as steep as that of the diode, and so no rule of thumb is appropriate. Newton's method may therefore be used in this case. From Eq. (6.9)

$$f'(V) = 3V^2 + 1$$

and using Eq. (6.7)

$$V_{n+1} = V_n - \frac{(V_n^3 + V_n - 3)}{(3V_n^2 + 1)} \tag{6.10}$$

If the nonlinear component were not present, the output voltage would be 3 volts. The nonlinear component causes additional current to flow through the 2 kΩ resistor connected to the battery, and so the output voltage will be less than this. Choosing $V_1 = 2.0$ volts as the initial guess, application of Eq. (6.10) using three decimal places gives the results shown in Table 6.2, and leads to the solution in five iterations.

Table 6.2

V_1	2.000
V_2	1.462
V_3	1.248
V_4	1.214
V_5	1.213
V_6	1.213

6.2   SMALL SIGNAL EQUIVALENT CIRCUITS

In the last section the *d.c. conditions* in simple nonlinear circuits were investigated. In this section the *a.c. conditions* will be considered, that is we shall seek methods for a.c. analysis in nonlinear circuits. Strictly, the phasor technique introduced in Chapter 3 is not appropriate for nonlinear circuits, since in general, the application of a sinusoidal voltage to a nonlinear circuit will not lead in the steady state to sinusoidal voltages and currents around the circuit. However, we shall see that if the a.c. analysis is restricted to *small signals*, then the phasor technique is applicable in providing a satisfactory engineering approximation to the true a.c. conditions in a nonlinear circuit.

Consider a linear resistor R to which a composite voltage $(V_Q + v)$ is applied. Here, V_Q will be assumed to be a d.c. voltage, while v will be taken as a varying or a.c. voltage superimposed on V_Q. Then the current which flows is given by:

$$I_Q + i = \frac{(V_Q + v)}{R} = \frac{V_Q}{R} + \frac{v}{R} \tag{6.11}$$

Eq. (6.11) shows that the d.c. condition $\left(I_Q = \frac{V_Q}{R}\right)$ and the a.c. condition $\left(i = \frac{v}{R}\right)$ add, in accordance with the principle of superposition, to give the total current flowing in the circuit. Now we turn to the case of a nonlinear component which has a terminal relationship $I = F(V)$. The equation corresponding to Eq. (6.11) is

$$I_Q + i = F(V_Q + v) \tag{6.12}$$

Expanding the right hand side of Eq. (6.12) as a Taylor Series leads to

$$I_Q + i = F(V_Q) + v F'(V_Q) + \frac{v^2}{2!} F''(V_Q) + \cdots \tag{6.13}$$

where the primes denote differentiation with respect to V. Providing the voltage v is sufficiently small, second and higher order terms in v can be ignored in Eq. (6.13), giving

$$I_Q + i = F(V_Q) + v F'(V_Q) \tag{6.14}$$

Comparing Eq. (6.14) with Eq. (6.11), we see that the d.c. condition is given by $I_Q = F(V_Q)$, while the a.c. condition is (approximately) given by $i = v F'(V_Q)$. Eq. (6.14) is a *linearised* version of Eq. (6.12), and is therefore only valid for small voltages v. However, providing v is appropriately small, Eq. (6.14) shows that the principle of superposition applies, and so all analysis techniques (such as phasors) which are based on linearity may be used. The quantities i and v are known as the *small signal* current and voltage. For the case of the linear resistor, $v/i = R$ as expected. However, for the nonlinear component, $v/i = 1/F'(V_Q) = r_s$. r_s is known as the *slope resistance*, or the *small signal a.c. resistance* of the nonlinear component, and it is a function of the quiescent voltage V_Q (and hence of I_Q).

To further clarify the above points, we may return to the circuit of Fig. 6.3, but add a source of sinusoidal a.c. signals as shown in Fig. 6.8. In the

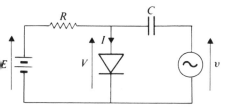

Fig. 6.8 Diode circuit with d.c. and a.c. inputs

absence of the a.c. source v, the voltage V and current I associated with the diode will be the quiescent voltage V_Q and current I_Q respectively, which may be established as described in the last section. The capacitor C in Fig. 6.8 is included to prevent the passage of d.c. current through the a.c. source. Thus, the d.c. condition in the circuit corresponds to the quiescent point Q on the diode characteristic shown in Fig. 6.9.

If now the a.c. source is considered, it will add a sinusoidal voltage to the quiescent voltage of the diode. If the capacitor C is so large that its reactance may be neglected, this a.c. voltage will be v. The sinusoidal variations of voltage will cause the operating point on the diode characteristic to move between the limiting points A and B in Fig. 6.9, where the time domain variations of the a.c. voltage are shown projected onto the diode characteristic. This movement of the operating point will lead to current variations which will not of course be sinusoidal because of the nonlinear diode characteristic. However, if the voltage excursions are sufficiently small, the current variations will be approximately sinusoidal. The magnitude of the current variation will then be determined approximately by the voltage v and the slope of the chord AB, and this slope may be taken to be that of the tangent of the diode characteristic at the point Q. Thus, if we write the diode terminal relationship as $I = F(V)$, then $i = vF'(V_Q)$, or $r_s = v/i = 1/F'(V_Q)$ as found previously.

Using Eq. (6.1)

$$I = I_s(e^{qV/kT} - 1) \tag{6.1}$$

Thus,

$$F'(V_Q) = \frac{dI}{dV}\bigg|_{V=V_Q} = I_s e^{qV_Q/kT} \cdot \frac{q}{kT} \tag{6.15}$$

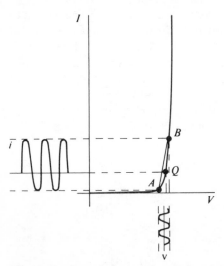

Fig. 6.9 Varying voltage superimposed on the diode characteristic

Now if the diode is forward biased, Eq. (6.1) may be approximated with little error by $I = I_s e^{qV/kT}$, and Eq. (6.15) becomes

$$F'(V_Q) = I_Q \cdot \frac{q}{kT}$$

and so $r_s = \dfrac{kT}{qI_Q} \,\Omega$. As previously remarked, $\dfrac{kT}{q} = 25 \times 10^{-3} \, V$, and so $r_s = \dfrac{25 \times 10^{-3}}{I_Q} \,\Omega$. For example, if a diode carries a quiescent current $I_Q = 1 \, mA$, in a particular circuit, then $r_s = \dfrac{25 \times 10^{-3}}{10^{-3}} = 25 \,\Omega$. In other words, the diode offers an a.c. slope resistance of 25 Ω. For the purposes of circuit analysis, the a.c. conditions in the circuit may therefore be determined by replacing the diode by a resistor of value 25 Ω. This resistor is known as the *small signal a.c. equivalent circuit of the diode.*

Thus, to establish the small signal a.c. conditions in a circuit incorporating two terminal nonlinear components, each such component may be represented by its small signal equivalent circuit which is simply a resistor of value given by the slope resistance evaluated at the quiescent point on the nonlinear characteristic. Under the assumption of small signals, the principle of superposition may be taken to apply, and the d.c. and a.c. conditions may then be added to give the complete analysis of the circuit.

Example

Determine the operating conditions for the diode in the circuit shown in Fig. 6.10.

We start by considering the d.c. conditions. Setting the a.c. source to zero, the circuit shown in Fig. 6.11(a) is obtained. (Note that the capacitor has been ignored since we are interested in the steady or quiescent voltages and currents in the circuit. These will be reached when the capacitor has fully charged, and in this condition it will pass no current, and may therefore be removed from circuit.)

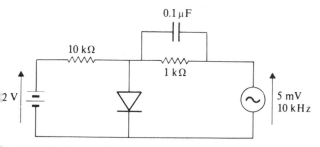

Fig. 6.10 Circuit example

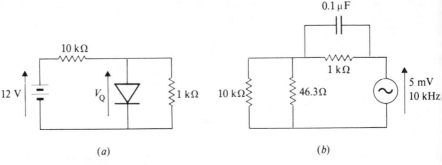

Fig. 6.11 (a) d.c. circuit, (b) a.c. equivalent circuit

Assuming a quiescent diode voltage of 0.6, the current through the 10 kΩ resistor is $\frac{(12-0.6)}{10^4} = 1.14$ mA. Of this, $\frac{0.6}{10^3} = 0.6$ mA flows through the 1 kΩ resistor, leaving $1.14 - 0.6 = 0.54$ mA flowing through the diode. Thus $V_Q = 0.6$V, $I_Q = 0.54$ mA. (The reader may care to check using Newton's method that with the diode as described previously $\left(I_s = 10^{-14}\text{A}, \frac{kT}{q} = 25 \text{ mV}\right)$, then $V_Q = 0.62$ V, $I_Q = 0.52$ mA to two decimal places, giving about 3% error in the assumption $V_Q = 0.6$ V.)

Turning now to the a.c. conditions, the small signal equivalent circuit of the diode will be a resistor of value $r_s = \frac{25 \times 10^{-3}}{0.54 \times 10^{-3}} = 46.3$ Ω. The small signal a.c. equivalent of Fig. 6.10 is therefore as shown in Fig. 6.11(b), where the battery d.c. source has been set to zero. Now the parallel combination of 10 kΩ and 46.3 Ω is about 46.1 Ω, while the 1 kΩ resistor and the capacitor have a combined impedance at 10 kHz of $\frac{10^3}{(1 + j2\pi \times 10^4 \times 10^3 \times 10^{-7})} = (24.7 - j155.2)$ Ω. Using the potential divider rule, the a.c. component of the diode voltage is

$$\frac{46.1}{46.1 + (24.7 - j155.2)} \times 5 \text{ mV}$$

$$= 0.56 + j1.23 \text{ mV}$$

$$\equiv 1.35 \text{ mV } \underline{/65.5°}$$

The magnitude of the a.c. diode current is therefore $\frac{1.35}{46.3} \approx 29.2 \ \mu\text{A}$.

Finally, one important question must be answered, namely, how small must the signals be for small signal a.c. analysis? Since the diode is one of the more common components for which such considerations apply, we shall concentrate on it to find an answer to the question. Now under conditions of forward bias, we may take

$$I_Q = I_s e^{40V_Q}$$

and

$$I_Q + i = I_s e^{40(V_Q+v)}$$

$$\therefore \quad i = I_s e^{40(V_Q+v)} - I_Q = I_Q e^{40v} - I_Q = I_Q(e^{40v} - 1) \tag{6.16}$$

Eq. (6.16) is a more accurate relationship between the voltage variation v and the resulting current variation i than that given by the slope of the diode characteristic, which has been seen to be

$$i = v \frac{d}{dV}(I_s e^{40V})|_{V=VQ} = v \cdot 40 I_s e^{40V_Q} = v \cdot 40 I_Q \tag{6.17}$$

A relative percentage error ϵ based upon the approximate current (Eq. (6.17)) and the more exact current (Eq. (6.16)) may now be defined, viz:

$$\epsilon = \frac{v \cdot 40 I_Q - I_Q(e^{40v} - 1)}{I_Q(e^{40v} - 1)} \times 100\%$$

$$= \left[\frac{40v}{e^{40v} - 1} - 1\right] \times 100\% \tag{6.18}$$

Eq. (6.18) may be evaluated for particular values of v. For example, with $v = 1$ mV, $\epsilon \approx -2\%$. In other words, there is of the order of 2% error in the use of the slope resistance as a *model* for the diode when there is a 1 mV voltage variation from the quiescent voltage. The error rises to 10% when $v \approx 5$ mV, whilst it exceeds 50% for voltages in excess of about 30 mV. It would appear then, that the small signal equivalent of a diode should only be used for variations of less than 5 mV, if an accuracy of better than 10% is to be achieved. In practice however, small signal equivalent circuits are used in circumstances where much larger voltage variations are considered. There are several justifications for this. One is that there is simply no easier way to analyse nonlinear circuits. If more accuracy is required, then numerical techniques must be used, which even for simple circuits usually necessitate the use of a digital computer. Another justification lies in the fact that modern circuit design practice utilises the concept of feedback. As previously remarked, feedback removes the dependence of circuit performance from those components which cannot be well defined, or are non-ideal. Diodes and transistors fall into these categories. Not only does feedback operate in the practical circuit, but it also influences the solution of the mathematical equations which characterise the circuit, thus reducing the need for high accuracy in characterising the components. We shall see feedback in action in a transistor circuit in the next section.

6.3   THE SMALL SIGNAL TRANSISTOR EQUIVALENT CIRCUIT

It is not the purpose of this book to consider detailed aspects of transistor operation or transistor circuit design. Rather, we are investigating ways in which circuits may be analysed so that their performance can be predicted. Because of the sophisticated mathematical tools available, and the simple ways that have been found to apply them, circuit analysis is much more simply accomplished than circuit design, which is largely innovative. Thus, in keeping with a text on Introductory Circuit Theory, the development of this section will make some simplifying assumptions on transistor operation, and will consider simple transistor circuits. The reader is referred to any of the many available textbooks for more detail in these subject areas.

Fig. 6.12 shows the symbol for a bipolar junction transistor, in this case an NPN type. The transistor is biased to a required operating point by the application of suitable d.c. voltages and currents to its base (B), collector (C) and emitter (E). These voltages and currents establish the quiescent or d.c. conditions of the transistor. The important property of the transistor is that quite large variations in collector current result from quite small variations in base current, and this clearly makes it an important device for use in amplifiers.

The d.c. conditions for a transistor are described by the Ebers–Moll equations, which in much simplified form may be stated as

$$I_E = I_s(e^{qV_{BE}/kT} - 1) \tag{6.19}$$

$$I_C = \alpha I_E \tag{6.20}$$

Equation (6.19) will be recognized as the diode equation, and indeed the base emitter junction of a transistor is a PN junction which is forward biased for amplifier applications of the device. Equation (6.20) indicates that a proportion α of the emitter current I_E flows from the collector. This factor α describes the current gain in common base configuration, and

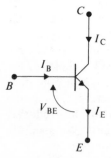

Fig. 6.12 Bipolar junction transistor symbol

typically has a value greater than 0.98, but less than unity. In addition to
the above two equations, Kirchhoff's Current Law also applies, giving,

$$I_E = I_C + I_B \qquad (6.21)$$

From Eq. (6.20) and Eq. (6.21)

$$I_E = \alpha I_E + I_B$$

$$\therefore \qquad I_E = \frac{I_B}{1 - \alpha}$$

and

$$I_C = \frac{\alpha I_B}{1 - \alpha} = \beta I_B \qquad (6.22)$$

Equation (6.22) relates the d.c. collector current to the d.c. base current
through the factor β, which is the common emitter current gain of the
transistor. If $\alpha > 0.98$, then $\beta > 49$, and in fact much higher values are
available in practice. Note that the value of β varies rapidly for only small
changes in α, and this leads to wide spreads in β in transistor manufacture.

Equations (6.19)–(6.22) provide sufficient information for the analysis
of transistor circuits to determine the quiescent conditions. For example,
Fig. 6.13 shows a simple transistor amplifier. To determine the d.c. conditions, note from Eq. (6.19) that for a wide range of the d.c. emitter
current I_E, the d.c. base–emitter voltage will be in the range 0.6–0.7 volts.
This point was established in section 6.2 when considering the diode. Thus,
taking $V_{BE} = 0.6$ volts, the voltage across the 100 kΩ resistor will be
$12 - 0.6 = 11.4$ volts, and the current through this resistor, which will be the
quiescent *base bias* current will be $I_B = \frac{11.4}{100} = 0.114$ mA. Taking a value of

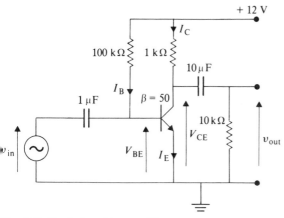

Fig. 6.13 Simple transistor amplifier

50 for β, Eq. (6.22) gives $I_C = 50 \times 0.114 = 5.7$ mA. The quiescent collector emitter voltage of the transistor is then given by $V_{CE} = 12 - 5.7 \times 10^{-3} \times 10^3 = 6.3$ volts. Note again that when charged, the capacitors will not pass any current, and so they may be disregarded for the purposes of determining d.c. conditions.

Turning now to the a.c. conditions, an equivalent circuit is needed for the transistor to simplify the calculations. In the case of the diode, this equivalent circuit was simply a resistor. However, a transistor has three terminals, compared with the two terminals of a diode, and so a more complex equivalent circuit can be expected. Indeed, small signal equivalent circuits for transistors can be extremely complex, but only a simple circuit will be developed here. What is required then, is some equivalent circuit which can be incorporated into the three terminal 'black box' shown in Fig. 6.14(a), and which provides a model for the small signal operation of the transistor shown in Fig. 6.14(b). In Fig. 6.13 it is seen that it is the a.c. input voltage v_{in} which provides the small signal variations of base voltage and current about the quiescent values, while the output voltage v_{out} is obtained by a.c. coupling the 10 kΩ load resistor via the 10 μF capacitor to the collector voltage variations.

There are several approaches to determining a suitable equivalent circuit for the transistor. In just the same way that either the Thévenin or Norton equivalent circuits may be determined for the same two terminal network, so several equivalent circuits exist for a transistor. We shall begin by rewriting Eq. (6.19) to Eq. (6.22) for small signal variations about the quiescent values. Thus, recalling the treatment of the diode, Eq. (6.19) gives:

$$i_e = v_{be} \cdot \frac{q}{kT} I_s e^{qV_{BE}/kT} = v_{be} \cdot \frac{qI_E}{kT} \qquad (6.23)$$

Eq. (6.23) defines r_e, the *small signal emitter slope resistance*:

$$r_e = \frac{v_{be}}{i_e} = \frac{kT}{qI_E} \qquad (6.24)$$

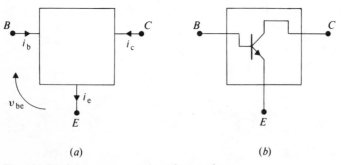

(a)   (b)

Fig. 6.14 Black box representation of a transistor

Corresponding to Eqs. (6.20), (6.21) and (6.22) we have

$$i_c = \alpha i_e \qquad (6.25)$$

$$i_e = i_c + i_b \qquad (6.26)$$

$$i_c = \beta i_b \qquad (6.27)$$

Strictly, the value of α and β are not the same as those which relate the d.c. currents, and indeed for small signal relationships, both α and β vary with the frequency of the signals. However, such variations will be ignored for simplicity.

Now Eq. (6.27) indicates that for a fixed (small signal) base current i_b, i_c must be constant. In particular, Eq. (6.27) is not a function of the small signal collector–emitter voltage v_{ce}. It seems reasonable therefore to model this fixed relationship between i_c and i_b by a current source connected between collector and emitter terminals of the 'black box' in Fig. 6.14(a). This is shown in Fig. 6.15. While i_c is a direct function of i_b according to Eq. (6.27), it is also a function of the small signal base–emitter voltage v_{be}. This can be seen using Eq. (6.24), since

$$v_{be} = r_e i_e$$

and using Eq. (6.26) and Eq. (6.27)

$$v_{be} = r_e(i_c + i_b) = r_e(\beta i_b + i_b) \simeq \beta r_e i_b \qquad (6.28)$$

assuming $\beta \gg 1$. Thus, either i_b or v_{be} can be taken as the small signal 'input' to the transistor, that is the controlling signal for the collector current. In many cases, particularly when using nodal analysis, it is preferable to assume that v_{be} is the controlling input of the transistor. In that case, Eq. (6.27) and Eq. (6.28) give

$$i_c = \beta i_b = \beta \frac{v_{be}}{\beta r_e} = \frac{1}{r_e} \cdot v_{be} = g_m v_{be} \qquad (6.29)$$

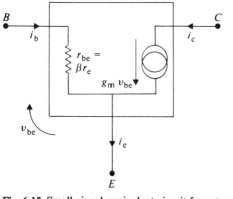

Fig. 6.15 Small signal equivalent circuit for a transistor

Here $g_m = \dfrac{1}{r_e}$ is known as the mutual conductance of the transistor, and

from Eq. (6.24), $g_m = \dfrac{qI_E}{kT} \approx \dfrac{qI_C}{kT}$. Finally, Eq. (6.28) also defines the small

signal base–emitter input resistance $r_{be} = \beta r_e$, and this is shown in Fig. 6.15.

It must be stressed that the equivalent circuit of Fig. 6.15 is the simplest circuit for a transistor. As such, it is somewhat restricted in its application. For example, like the diode equivalent circuit, there are no components which model frequency limitations of the device. In addition, in a practical transistor any collector–emitter and collector–base voltage variations would influence both collector and base current, and these effects together with the bulk resistance of the semiconductor material must be modelled in a more sophisticated equivalent circuit. Fig. 6.16 shows such a circuit, known as the hybrid-π equivalent circuit of a transistor, but its derivation is outside the scope of this book.

We may now return to consider the a.c. conditions in the circuit shown in Fig. 6.13, using the simple equivalent circuit of Fig. 6.15. Taking $\dfrac{q}{kT} = 40$,

and with $I_C = 5.7\,\text{mA}$, $g_m = 40 \times 5.7 = 228\,\text{mA/V}$. Thus $r_e = \dfrac{10^3}{228} \approx 4.4\,\Omega$, and

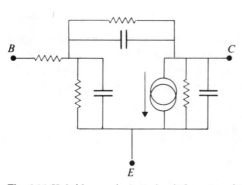

Fig. 6.16 Hybrid-π equivalent circuit for a transistor

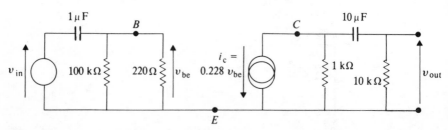

Fig. 6.17 Small signal equivalent circuit for the simple transistor amplifier

$r_{be} = 50 \times 4.4 = 220\ \Omega$. Recalling that the use of a small signal equivalent circuit permits the benefits of the principle of superposition, Fig. 6.13 may now be redrawn with the 12 volt d.c. supply set to zero, that is with the supply line grounded, and with the equivalent circuit replacing the transistor. This is shown in Fig. 6.17. As an example, the small signal voltage gain of the circuit will be calculated assuming a sinusoidal input voltage of frequency 1 kHz. The 100 kΩ base bias resistor in parallel with $r_{be} = 220\ \Omega$ may be ignored, and so

$$v_{be} = v_{in} \frac{220}{220 - \dfrac{j1}{2\pi \times 10^3 \times 10^{-6}}} = v_{in}(0.656 + j0.475)$$

Now $i_c = 0.228\ v_{be} = v_{in}(0.149 + j0.108)$. At 1 kHz, the 10 μF capacitor has a reactance of $\dfrac{-1}{(2\pi \times 10^3 \times 10^{-5})} \simeq -16\ \Omega$, which may be ignored compared with the 10 kΩ a.c. load resistor. The collector current i_c therefore flows through the parallel combination of the two resistors in the output circuit, and so

$$v_{out} = -i_c \times \frac{(1 \times 10)}{(1 + 10)} \times 10^3$$

$$= -v_{in}(0.149 + j0.108) \times \frac{10}{11} \times 10^3$$

i.e., $\qquad\qquad v_{out} = -(135 + j98.2)v_{in} \equiv 167\ v_{in}\underline{/-144^\circ} \qquad\qquad$ (6.30)

In practice, the circuit configuration of Fig. 6.13 is seldom used for a variety of reasons. In particular, both the d.c. and a.c. conditions in the circuit are heavily dependent on β, which can have a high manufacturing spread, and the circuit also has poor temperature stability. Further, the small signal voltage gain given by Eq. (6.30) must be treated with suspicion. For all but the smallest input signals, the magnitude of the gain (167) implies that sizeable variations in the collector current of the transistor will occur as the input voltage magnitude is increased. Thus, the value of g_m will vary as the current varies. This has two implications. First, the figure of 167, (as expected from previous arguments) will no longer be valid, and second, the output waveform will suffer increasing distortion as larger excursions are made on the nonlinear transistor characteristic.

The circuit shown in Fig. 6.18 enjoys popular use as a means of overcoming some of the drawbacks of the previous circuit. Providing the current flowing through the potentiometer bias resistors R_1 and R_2 is much greater than the base current taken by the transistor, the d.c. base voltage will be fixed at $V_B = \dfrac{V_{CC} \cdot R_2}{(R_1 + R_2)}$. Taking V_{BE} for the transistor to be 0.6 volts, the d.c. emitter voltage will therefore be $V_E = V_B - 0.6$, which will establish

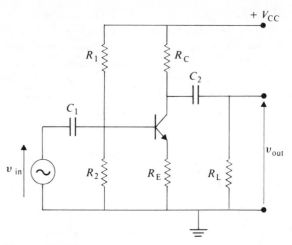

Fig. 6.18 Transistor amplifier

a quiescent emitter current of $I_E = \dfrac{V_E}{R_E}$. Now $I_C = \alpha I_E \approx I_E$, therefore

$$I_C = \frac{\left[\dfrac{V_{CC} \cdot R_2}{(R_1 + R_2)}\right] - 0.6}{R_E} \tag{6.31}$$

and finally $V_C = V_{CC} - R_C I_C$. Eq. (6.31) shows that the collector current is independent of β. (Strictly, I_C is dependent on α, since $I_C = \alpha I_E$. However, unlike variations in β, spreads in α are small, and have minimal effect on the quiescent voltages and currents in this circuit.) To determine the small signal voltage gain of this circuit, the d.c. supply V_{CC} is reduced to zero, and the equivalent circuit is substituted for the transistor. This is shown in Fig. 6.19. For the purpose of this example, the output coupling capacitor will be assumed sufficiently large for its reactance to be ignored, so that the

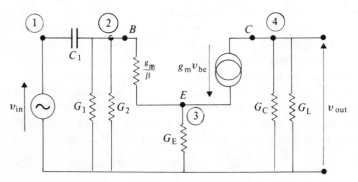

Fig. 6.19 Small signal equivalent circuit for the transistor amplifier

collector and load resistors may be considered to be in parallel in the a.c. equivalent circuit. The circuit of Fig. 6.19 is more complicated than that obtained from the previous circuit, and so nodal analysis will be used to find the solution. The nodes have been numbered in Fig. 6.19, and the conductances $G_1 = \dfrac{1}{R_1}$, etc., have been appended in anticipation. The difference between this problem and those discussed in Chapter 5 is that the circuit of Fig. 6.19 includes a dependent source, namely the voltage controlled current source defined by the mutual conductance g_m. To begin with we may ignore this dependent source which is introduced by the *active* component (that is, the transistor), and simply write the nodal equations for the passive components in the circuit. These are:

$$
\begin{bmatrix} i_1 \\ i_2 \\ i_3 \\ i_4 \end{bmatrix} =
\begin{bmatrix}
j\omega C_1 & -j\omega C_1 & 0 & 0 \\
-j\omega C_1 & \left(G_1 + G_2 + \dfrac{g_m}{\beta} + j\omega C_1\right) & -\dfrac{g_m}{\beta} & 0 \\
0 & -\dfrac{g_m}{\beta} & \left(G_E + \dfrac{g_m}{\beta}\right) & 0 \\
0 & 0 & 0 & (G_C + G_L)
\end{bmatrix}
\begin{bmatrix} v_1 \\ v_2 \\ v_3 \\ v_4 \end{bmatrix}
$$

$$(6.32)$$

The effect of introducing the dependent current source will be to change the current balance equations at node 3 (the emitter) and node 4 (the collector). The current flowing *away* from node 3 will be *reduced by* $g_m v_{be} = g_m(v_2 - v_3) = g_m v_2 - g_m v_3$, while that flowing away from node 4 will be *increased* by the same amount. These additional currents may therefore be incorporated into the right hand side of Eq. (6.32) as shown in Eq. (6.33).

$$
\begin{bmatrix} i_1 \\ i_2 \\ i_3 \\ i_4 \end{bmatrix} =
\begin{bmatrix}
j\omega C_1 & -j\omega C_1 & 0 & 0 \\
-j\omega C_1 & \left(G_1 + G_2 + \dfrac{g_m}{\beta} + j\omega C_1\right) & -\dfrac{g_m}{\beta} & 0 \\
0 & -\dfrac{g_m}{\beta} - g_m & \left(G_E + \dfrac{g_m}{\beta} + g_m\right) & 0 \\
0 & g_m & -g_m & (G_C + G_L)
\end{bmatrix}
\begin{bmatrix} v_1 \\ v_2 \\ v_3 \\ v_4 \end{bmatrix}
$$

$$(6.33)$$

Then $v_4 = \dfrac{\Delta_{14}}{\Delta_{11}} v_1$, where

$$
\Delta_{14} = -\begin{vmatrix}
-j\omega C_1 & \left(G_1 + G_2 + \dfrac{g_m}{\beta} + j\omega C_1\right) & -\dfrac{g_m}{\beta} \\
0 & -\dfrac{g_m}{\beta} - g_m & \left(G_E + \dfrac{g_m}{\beta} + g_m\right) \\
0 & g_m & -g_m
\end{vmatrix}
$$

$$= j\omega C_1 \begin{vmatrix} -\dfrac{g_m}{\beta} - g_m & \left(G_E + \dfrac{g_m}{\beta} + g_m\right) \\ g_m & -g_m \end{vmatrix}$$

$$= j\omega C_1 \left[g_m\left(\dfrac{g_m}{\beta} + g_m\right) - g_m\left(G_E + \dfrac{g_m}{\beta} + g_m\right) \right] = -j\omega C_1 g_m G_E$$

and

$$\Delta_{11} = \begin{vmatrix} \left(G_1 + G_2 + \dfrac{g_m}{\beta} + j\omega C_1\right) & -\dfrac{g_m}{\beta} & 0 \\ -\dfrac{g_m}{\beta} - g_m & \left(G_E + \dfrac{g_m}{\beta} + g_m\right) & 0 \\ g_m & -g_m & (G_C + G_L) \end{vmatrix}$$

$$= (G_C + G_L) \begin{vmatrix} \left(G_1 + G_2 + \dfrac{g_m}{\beta} + j\omega C_1\right) & -\dfrac{g_m}{\beta} \\ -\dfrac{g_m}{\beta} - g_m & \left(G_E + \dfrac{g_m}{\beta} + g_m\right) \end{vmatrix}$$

$$= (G_C + G_L) \left[\left(G_1 + G_2 + \dfrac{g_m}{\beta} + j\omega C_1\right)\left(G_E + \dfrac{g_m}{\beta} + g_m\right) - \dfrac{g_m}{\beta}\left(\dfrac{g_m}{\beta} + g_m\right) \right]$$

$$= (G_C + G_L) \left[\left(G_1 + G_2 + j\omega C_1\right)\left(G_E + \dfrac{g_m}{\beta} + g_m\right) + \dfrac{g_m}{\beta} G_E \right]$$

Thus,

$$v_4 = \dfrac{-j\omega C_1 g_m G_E \cdot v_1}{(G_C + G_L)\left[(G_1 + G_2 + j\omega C_1)\left(G_E + \dfrac{g_m}{\beta} + g_m\right) + \dfrac{g_m G_E}{\beta} \right]} \tag{6.34}$$

If

$$\beta \gg 1 \tag{6.35}$$

and

$$G_E \ll g_m \tag{6.36}$$

then Eq. (6.34) simplifies to

$$\dfrac{v_{out}}{v_{in}} = \dfrac{-j\omega C_1 G_E}{(G_C + G_L)(G_1 + G_2 + j\omega C_1)} \tag{6.37}$$

Eq. (6.37) is clearly not a function of β or g_m. For Eq. (6.37) to apply, β and g_m do not need to have specific values, but need to be of such magnitude that Eqs. (6.35) and (6.36) apply. Thus the operation of the circuit of Fig. 6.14 is largely independent of the parameters of the transistor. Furthermore, since the precise value of g_m does not appear in Eq. (6.37), g_m variation will neither affect the precision of Eq. (6.37), nor the purity of the output signal in the practical circuit. This is because the circuit of Fig. 6.18 incorporates negative feedback, introduced by the emitter resistor R_E. The controlling a.c. input to the transistor is v_{be}, which is the difference between the small signal a.c. base and emitter voltages. In the circuit of Fig. 6.13, the emitter voltage is zero, while in Fig. 6.18, it will be $v_e = i_e R_E \simeq i_c R_E$. Now $i_c = g_m v_{be} = g_m(v_b - v_e)$, and so $i_c = g_m(v_b - i_c R_E)$. This leads to $i_c(1 + g_m R_E) = g_m v_b$, whence $i_c = g_m v_b/(1 + g_m R_E)$. Thus, providing $g_m R_E \gg 1$ (i.e. Eq. (6.36)), $i_c = \dfrac{v_b}{R_E}$. In other words the effect of the emitter resistor is to feed back to the input of the transistor a voltage proportional to collector current. The sense of this voltage is such as to reduce the controlling input to the transistor, that is it introduces negative feedback. The relationship between the collector current and the base voltage therefore depends on the emitter resistor, and as we have seen, providing that g_m is sufficiently large, this may be taken to be an exclusive dependence.

6.4 SUMMARY

The apparent difficulties which nonlinear components can introduce into circuit analysis have been effectively discounted in this chapter. It has been seen that even the simplest nonlinear circuits are often characterized by equations which have no analytic solution. However, two approaches are available to solve such problems. On the one hand a numerical technique can be used to solve the problem by iteration. Newton's method has been discussed as one such technique. On the other hand, rules of thumb may be devised for components such as the diode and the transistor, based upon the realisation that when forward biased, the diode voltage and the transistor base–emitter voltage will lie in the range 0.6–0.7 volts for a wide range of diode or emitter currents respectively.

Despite the nonlinear characteristics of many practical components, it has also been shown that for small signal excursions, the characteristics may be linearised, giving rise to the concept of the a.c. small signal equivalent circuit. Furthermore, since modern circuit design utilizes feedback to reduce the dependence of circuit performance on the precise parameters of such components, the small signal restriction which justifies the applicability of the equivalent circuits may be relaxed. All the tools of linear circuit analysis are therefore available in the analysis of nonlinear circuits, and in the majority of cases they will provide a solution which will be an acceptable engineering approximation to reality.

Problems

1. A nonlinear resistor has the following characteristic:

voltage (V)	0.5	1.0	1.5	2.0	2.5	3.0
current (mA)	−2.88	0	0.38	5.0	12.63	24.0

The component is connected in series with a 1 kΩ resistor across a 10 V battery. Find the current which flows, and the voltage developed across the nonlinear resistor.
(Answer: Approximately 7.9 mA, 2.2 V)

2. A diode, having terminal characteristics $I = 10^{-14}(e^{40V} - 1)$ is connected in series with a 250 Ω resistor and a 5 V battery with the diode forward biassed. Calculate the resistor voltage to one decimal place.
(Answer: 4.3 V)

3. Two nonlinear components having terminal characteristics $I_1 = V_0^3$ and $I_2 = \sqrt{V_0}$ respectively are connected in parallel with a current generator as shown in Fig. 6.20. Find the voltage V_0 to two decimal places.
(Answer: 1.41 V)

4. A diode carries a quiescent d.c. current of 4 mA. If a current $i = 3 \times 10^{-6} \sin \omega t$ A is superimposed on this d.c. current, calculate the peak value of the time varying voltage which is developed across the diode.
(Answer: Approximately 19 μV)

5. Find the approximate a.c. voltage developed across the diode in Fig. 6.21.
(Answer: 1.3 mV $/-84°$)

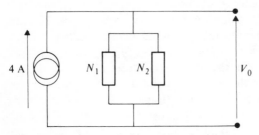

Fig. 6.20 Circuit example for problem 3

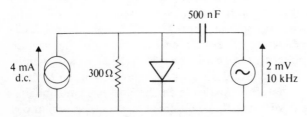

Fig. 6.21 Circuit example for problem 5

6. Find the small signal gain and phase shift of the amplifier shown in Fig. 6.22, at 1 kHz. Assume that the transistor has a β of 100.

$$\left(\text{Answer: } \frac{|V_2|}{|V_1|} = 236, \ \phi = 42°\right)$$

7. Determine the quiescent collector current in the emitter follower circuit shown in Fig. 6.23, and hence find the approximate magnitude and phase of the a.c. output voltage V_o in the terms of V_1 at a frequency of 250 Hz. Assume $\beta = 150$ for the transistor.

$$\left(\text{Answer: } 5 \text{ mA}, \ \frac{|V_o|}{|V_1|} = 0.7, \ \phi = \underline{/43°}\right)$$

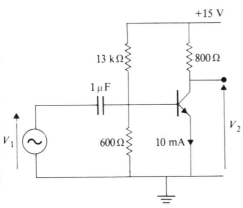

Fig. 6.22 Amplifier circuit (problem 6)

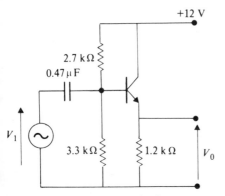

Fig. 6.23 Emitter follower circuit (problem 7)

7

A.C. POWER

It was seen in Chapter 1 that when a sinusoidal voltage is applied to a resistor, the average power dissipated in the resistor may be found as the product of the r.m.s. voltage and the r.m.s. value of the current which flows. In this chapter we shall consider the calculation of the power dissipated in a circuit which is not resistive. In such a case the current and voltage will not be in phase, and it is found that the useful power dissipated in the circuit is not simply given by the product of the r.m.s. voltage and current magnitudes, and in fact may be less than this product. Such considerations are important for example in the design of amplifiers where the output load (possibly a loudspeaker) does not offer a resistive impedance over its specified frequency range, and yet the performance ssessment of the amplifier will be based on the useful power dissipated in the load. They are perhaps even more important for the power engineer. The electricity generation authorities receive an income related to the power consumed by its customers. Clearly, if the power consumed by a customer is less than the product of the r.m.s. voltage and current magnitudes, this implies that for a given supply voltage, too much current is being provided, representing an uneconomic utilization of transmission equipment capacity, and steps must be taken to correct the situation.

Later in the chapter a related topic of great importance will be discussed, namely how to extract the maximum power from an energy source. This topic is also of interest in amplifier design, where special equalization networks are often constructed to optimize load power.

7.1 COMPLEX POWER

The resistor shown in Fig. 7.1 has a voltage $v = V_m \cos(\omega t + \theta)$ applied to its terminals. A current $i = I_m \cos(\omega t + \theta)$ will flow, where $I_m = \dfrac{V_m}{R}$. Following the development in Chapter 1, the instantaneous power dissipated in the resistor will be $p = V_m I_m \cos^2(\omega t + \theta)$, and the average power P over one cycle $\left(\text{of duration } T = \dfrac{2\pi}{\omega}\right)$ of the sinusoidal waveform is

$$P = \frac{1}{T}\int_0^T V_m I_m \cos^2(\omega t + \theta)\, dt = \frac{V_m I_m}{2} = V_{rms} I_{rms} \tag{7.1}$$

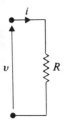

Fig. 7.1 Resistor

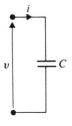

Fig. 7.2 Capacitor

Turning now to the capacitor shown in Fig. 7.2, with $v = V_m \cos(\omega t + \theta)$ then $i = \dfrac{C\,dv}{dt} = -\omega C V_m \sin(\omega t + \theta) = I_m \sin(\omega t + \theta)$, and so the instantaneous power is given by

$$p = -V_m I_m \cos(\omega t + \theta)\sin(\omega t + \theta) = -\frac{V_m I_m}{2}\sin[2(\omega t + \theta)] \qquad (7.2)$$

In this case, the average power is given by

$$P = -\frac{1}{T}\int_0^T \frac{V_m I_m}{2}\sin[2(\omega t + \theta)]\,dt = 0 \qquad (7.3)$$

Eq. (7.3) shows that the average power dissipated in a capacitor is zero. This is because, as discussed in Chapter 4, the average energy stored in a capacitor is zero under sinusoidal excitation. Thus, if a capacitor is connected to an a.c. supply, current will flow, but no power will be consumed on average. Indeed, as Eq. (7.2) shows, the capacitor will alternately act as a sink and a source of power as p changes sign. It is left to the reader to show that the same is true of the inductor. Eq. (7.2) shows that the instantaneous power supplied to the capacitor will have a maximum value of $\dfrac{V_m I_m}{2} = V_{rms}I_{rms}$ and this is known as the *reactive power*, to differentiate it from the *real power* which is dissipated in a resistor.

Having considered the two extreme cases of power supplied to purely resistive and purely reactive components, we may now investigate the general case shown in Fig. 7.3. This represents a general two terminal circuit. We shall assume $v = V_m \cos(\omega t + \theta)$, and $i = I_m \cos(\omega t + \theta + \phi)$ where ϕ is the phase angle *between* the current and voltage waveforms. Thus, if ϕ is positive (negative) the circuit is said to be capacitive (inductive). In this case, the instantaneous power is given by

$$p = V_m I_m \cos(\omega t + \theta)\cos(\omega t + \theta + \phi)$$

$$= V_m I_m \cos(\omega t + \theta)[\cos(\omega t + \theta)\cos\phi - \sin(\omega t + \theta)\sin\phi]$$

i.e.,

$$p = [V_m I_m \cos\phi]\cos^2(\omega t + \theta) - \left[\frac{V_m I_m}{2}\sin\phi\right]\sin[2(\omega t + \theta)] \qquad (7.4)$$

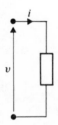

Fig. 7.3 General two terminal circuit

The first term on the right hand side of Eq. (7.4) is seen to be similar to the integrand of Eq. (7.1), while the second term is similar to that of Eq. (7.3), and so the average power is given by

$$P = \frac{V_m I_m}{2} \cos \phi = V_{rms} I_{rms} \cos \phi \qquad (7.5)$$

The first term on the right hand side of Eq. (7.4) therefore corresponds to the real, resistive, or useful power dissipated in the load, and $P = V_{rms} I_{rms} \cos \phi$ has the units of Watts in the usual way. The quantity $\cos \phi$ is known as the *power factor* of the circuit. ϕ is the angle between the current and the voltage waveforms, and the power factor is the factor by which the *apparent power*, $V_{rms} I_{rms}$ must be multiplied to give the real power. To stress that the product $V_{rms} I_{rms}$ is apparent power, it is usually measured in Volt-Amperes, or VA rather than Watts.

Finally, comparing the second term on the right hand side of Eq. (7.4) with Eq. (7.2), it is seen that in the general circuit, a reactive power of $\frac{V_m I_m}{2} \sin \phi = V_{rms} I_{rms} \sin \phi$ is supplied. This reactive power is measured in Volt-Amperes reactive, or VAr (pronounced 'Vars').

To summarize, if a sinusoidal voltage V_{rms} and current I_{rms} are supplied to a circuit, and a phase shift ϕ exists between the current and the voltage waveforms, then:

$$\left.\begin{array}{ll} \text{Apparent power (VA)} & = V_{rms} I_{rms} \\ \text{Real power (W)} & = V_{rms} I_{rms} \cos \phi \\ \text{Reactive power (VAr)} & = V_{rms} I_{rms} \sin \phi \end{array}\right\} \qquad (7.6)$$

The results of Eq. (7.6) have been developed by manipulating the time domain descriptions of the sinusoidal voltage and current applied to a general two terminal circuit. However, they may also be found by considering the phasor counterparts of these time domain quantities. For example, let $V = V_{rms} e^{j\theta}$ and $I = I_{rms} e^{j(\theta + \phi)}$ be the phasors corresponding to the time domain voltage and current respectively. (Note that the magnitudes of the phasors have been taken to be the r.m.s. amplitudes of the corresponding time domain quantities.) First we take the complex conjugate of I, simply by reversing its angle. Thus $I^* = I_{rms} e^{-j(\theta + \phi)}$, where the asterisk denotes conjugate. Taking the product of V and I^*, we have

$$S = VI^* = V_{rms} I_{rms} e^{-j\phi}$$

i.e.,

$$S = V_{rms} I_{rms} \cos \phi - j V_{rms} I_{rms} \sin \phi \qquad (7.7)$$

Here S is known as the *complex power*. Noting Eq. (7.6), it is seen that by forming the product $S = VI^*$,

$$\left.\begin{array}{ll} \text{Apparent power} = |S| \\ \text{Real power} \quad\;\; = Re[S] \\ \text{Reactive power} = Im[S] \end{array}\right\} \qquad (7.8)$$

The results in Eq. (7.8) are particularly satisfying, since they show that the phasor technique may be extended to the calculation of power. However, the reader should be aware that it is Eq. (7.6) which arises from a rigorous treatment of the topic. Eq. (7.8) is merely a development of Eq (7.6), using the artifice of taking the conjugate of the current phasor, simply to give the required result.

The negative sign associated with the reactive power in Eq. (7.7) is simply an indication that the circuit is capacitive. This is clearly illustrated in Eq. (7.2). Conversely, if the reactive power obtained from Eq. (7.8) is found to be positive, then the circuit will be inductive, since ϕ must be negative, that is the current must be lagging the voltage.

Example

When a sinusoidal input of frequency 10 kHz is applied to a hi-fi amplifier a peak to peak output voltage of 44 volts is developed across the loud-speaker, lagging the input by 10°. The current is found to be 5.2 amperes pk–pk lagging the input by 24°. Calculate (i) the apparent, real and reactive power, (ii) the power factor, (iii) the impedance of the loudspeaker.

The power calculations require that the voltage and current be expressed by their r.m.s. values. The loudspeaker voltage is 44 volts pk–pk, which is $\dfrac{44}{(2\sqrt{2})}$ volts r.m.s. = 15.56 volts. Similarly, the r.m.s. current will be $\dfrac{5.2}{(2\sqrt{2})}$ amperes r.m.s. = 1.84 amps. Using the polar notation, the voltage and current phasors are given by

$$V = 15.56 \, \underline{/-10°}$$
$$I = 1.84 \, \underline{/-24°}$$

Thus, $I^* = 1.84 \, \underline{/24°}$, and

$$S = (15.56 \times 1.84) \, \underline{/(-10° + 24°)} = 28.63 \, \underline{/14°}$$

Using Eq. (7.8), it will be seen that:

$$\text{apparent power} = |S| = \underline{28.63 \, \text{VA}}$$
$$\text{real power} = |S| \cos 14° = \underline{27.78 \, \text{W}}$$
$$\text{reactive power} = |S| \sin 14° = \underline{6.93 \, \text{VAr}}$$

Since the reactive power has positive sign, the loudspeaker appears inductive at the input frequency. In fact the current is lagging the voltage by 14°.

The power factor is simply $\underline{\cos 14° = 0.97}$. This power factor would be said to be *lagging* to indicate that the current is lagging the voltage in the load.

Finally, the impedance of the load is obtained from

$$Z \times 1.84 \underline{/-24°} = 15.56 \underline{/-10°}$$

i.e.,

$$Z = 8.46 \ \Omega \underline{/14°}$$
$$= (8.21 + j2.05) \ \Omega$$

When an impedance is expressed in rectangular form $Z = R + jX$ as in the above example, it can be thought of as comprising a resistor of value R in series with a reactance X. This is shown in Fig. 7.4. This configuration is of course a circuit *model*, and is not necessarily an indication of the actual circuit configuration of the impedance. Now by Ohm's Law,

$$V = (R + jX)I$$

The complex power S is then

$$S = VI^* = (R + jX)II^* \qquad (7.9)$$

Suppose $I = |I|e^{j\theta}$ and so $I^* = |I|e^{-j\theta}$. Then $II^* = |I|^2$, and Eq. (7.9) becomes

$$S = (R + jX)|I|^2 = |I|^2R + j|I|^2 \ X \qquad (7.10)$$

The power may therefore be determined directly from the impedance, and the magnitude of the current. Referring back to Eq. (7.8), it is seen that the real power is dissipated by the real part of the impedance Z, while the reactive power is determined by its reactive part. It is important to note that, for example, the real power in Eq. (7.10) *cannot* be written as $\dfrac{|V|^2}{R}$ (as is the case for the resistive circuits), since Fig. 7.4 shows that the voltage V is not developed across R alone, but across the total impedance. An expression for complex power similar to Eq. (7.10), but involving V can be obtained by modelling not the impedance, but the corresponding ad-

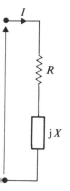

Fig. 7.4 Model for a general impedance

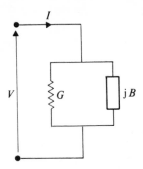

Fig. 7.5 Model for a general admittance

mittance $Y = \dfrac{1}{Z} = G + jB$. This is shown in Fig. 7.5. In this case the admittance is modelled by a conductance G in parallel with a susceptance B.

Then

$$I = (G + jB)V$$

and

$$VI^* = (G - jB)VV^*$$

i.e.,

$$S = (G - jB)|V|^2 = |V|^2 G - j|V|^2 B \qquad (7.11$$

The real and reactive power expressed by Eq. (7.10) and Eq. (7.11) must of course, be the same. This is simply shown, since for example

$$|I|^2 R = \frac{|V|^2}{|Z|} R = |V|^2 \frac{R}{(R^2 + X^2)} = |V|^2 G$$

Example

A coil has a winding resistance of $120\,\Omega$ and an inductance of $1\,H$ Determine the power factor and the real power which will be dissipated i the coil when it is connected to the 240 volt 50 Hz domestic mains supply What will be the effect of connecting a $10\,\mu F$ capacitor across the coil?

At 50 Hz, the coil will have an impedance

$$Z = (120 + j100\pi)\Omega \equiv 336.3\,\Omega\ \underline{/69.1^\circ}$$

Thus, the current in the coil will lag the voltage by $\underline{/69.1^\circ}$ and so th power factor will be $\cos(69.1^\circ) = \underline{0.34\ \text{lagging}}$.

The equivalent admittance of the coil is

$$Y = \frac{1}{(120 + j100\pi)} = (1.06 \times 10^{-3} - j2.78 \times 10^{-3})\ S$$

Using Eq. (7.11), the real power dissipated in the coil will be $(240)^2 \times 1.06 \times 10^{-3} = \underline{61.1W}$.

The effect of connecting a capacitor in parallel with the coil will be to change the susceptive part of the total load admittance. The conductive part will not be affected, and so the real power dissipated in the load will remain the same. The susceptance of a $10\,\mu\text{F}$ capacitor at $50\,\text{Hz}$ is $100\pi \times 10^{-5} = 3.14 \times 10^{-3}\,\text{S}$. The total load admittance will therefore become

$$Y = (1.06 \times 10^{-3} - \text{j}2.78 \times 10^{-3}) + \text{j}3.14 \times 10^{-3} = (1.06 \times 10^{-3} + \text{j}0.36 \times 10^{-3})\,\text{S}$$

or in modulus argument form:

$$Y = 1.12\,\text{mS}\ \underline{/18.8°}$$

In this case the current leads the voltage by 18.8°, and so the power factor has become $\cos(18.8°) = \underline{0.95\ \text{leading}}$.

One important point to note from the above example is that the load power factor was changed by connecting a reactive component across it. Power generation authorities usually stipulate a minimum power factor which loads to be connected to the mains supply must meet. This leads to the most economic utilization of the transmission equipment. Recalling that the power factor is the factor by which the apparent power must be multiplied to give the real power, it will be seen that in the last example the initial power factor of 0.34 implies that the current supplied to the load would be $\dfrac{1}{0.34} \approx 3$ times its value if unity power factor were achieved. It is easy to understand the authorities concern where large powers are involved. The $10\,\mu\text{F}$ capacitor connected across the load in the example improves the situation by providing a substantial *power factor correction*. Indeed, the reader may care to check that an $8.85\,\mu\text{F}$ capacitor would achieve unity power factor, which would represent the ideal load. This is because in such a case the voltage and current in the load would be in phase, that is the load would appear resistive to the supply.

Thus we see that power factor correction is tantamount to bringing a load impedance near to resonance at the supply frequency. If resonance is achieved, then this corresponds to unity power factor. Industrial loads tend to be inductive, reflecting the widespread use of wound components such as transformers, rotating machines, starting inductors for fluorescent lamps and so on, and in such cases power factor correction is often required.

7.2 POWER MATCHING

In this section, the problem of extracting the maximum power from a source will be investigated. The source might be a radio antenna, an amplifier, a telephone cable and so on. Whatever the actual source, it is

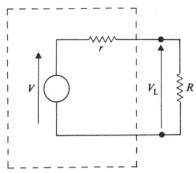

Fig. 7.6 Resistive source with resistive load

usually possible to model it by a Thévenin or Norton equivalent. Fig. 7.6 shows the simplest case of a resistive source impedance r and a resistive load R. The problem is to find the value of load resistance R which will maximise the power supplied to it.

The voltage developed across the load is given by

$$V_L = \frac{R}{R+r} \cdot V$$

The power dissipated in R is

$$P = \frac{|V_L|^2}{R} = \frac{|V|^2 R}{(R+r)^2} \tag{7.12}$$

Differentiating Eq. (7.12) with respect to R to find the extremum,

$$\frac{dP}{dR} = |V|^2 \left\{ \frac{(R+r)^2 - 2R(R+r)}{(R+r)^4} \right\} = |V|^2 \frac{(r-R)}{(R+r)^3}$$

and $\frac{dP}{dR} = 0$, when $R = r$. In fact this corresponds to a maximum value of P, which from Eq. (7.12) is seen to be $P_{max} = \frac{|V|^2}{4r}$. Thus by selecting a load resistance equal to the source resistance, the maximum power will be dissipated in the load, which is then said to be *power matched.*

The power available from a source does not depend on the particular equivalent circuit used for that source, and precisely the same result is obtained if the Norton equivalent is used instead of the Thévenin equivalent in Fig. 7.6. However, since the Norton current source will have value $I = \frac{V}{r}$, then $P_{max} = \frac{|V|^2}{4r} = \frac{|I|^2 r}{4}$.

Example

Find the value of load resistor for power matching in the circuit shown in Fig. 7.7(a).

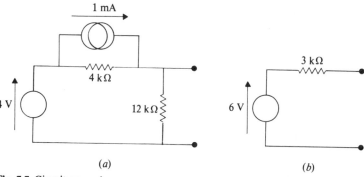

(a)

(b)

Fig. 7.7 Circuit example

Initially the Thévenin equivalent circuit will be found. Using the principle of superposition to find the open circuit voltage in Fig. 7.7(a)

$$V_{OC} = 4\frac{12}{4+12} + 10^{-3}\left(\frac{4\times12}{4+12}\right) \times 10^3 = 6\text{ volts}$$

The Thévenin source resistance is found by setting the sources in Fig. 7.7(a) to zero and calculating the resistance seen from the terminals. This is $\frac{4\times12}{4+12)\text{ k}\Omega} = 3\text{ k}\Omega$. The Thévenin equivalent is shown in Fig. 7.7(b). From the earlier discussion, a load resistor of $3\text{ k}\Omega$ is therefore required to extract the maximum power from the circuit, and that power will be $P_{max} = \frac{6^2}{(4\times3\times10^3)} = 3\text{ mW}$.

In the more general case, a source will have a complex source impedance $r + jx$, where x may be positive (inductive) or negative (capacitive). This is shown in Fig. 7.8. The problem now is to determine the two parameters R and X such that the maximum *real* power is dissipated in the load impedance $(R + jX)$.

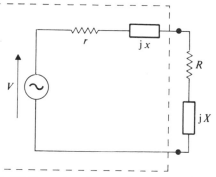

Fig. 7.8 Generator with complex source and load impedance

The current flowing in the load is

$$I = \frac{V}{(R + jX) + (r + jx)} = \frac{V}{(R + r) + j(X + x)}$$

Thus the real power dissipated in the load will be

$$P = |I|^2 R = \frac{|V|^2 R}{(R + r)^2 + (X + x)^2} \tag{7.13}$$

Concentrating first on the variable X, we have

$$\frac{dP}{dX} = \frac{-|V|^2 R \cdot 2(X + x)}{[(R + r)^2 + (X + x)^2]^2} = 0 \text{ for extrema} \tag{7.14}$$

Eq. (7.14) yields $X = -x$ for an extremum, which in fact corresponds to a maximum for P. Substituting $X = -x$ in Eq. (7.13) leads to

$$P = \frac{|V|^2 R}{(R + r)^2}$$

and this is identical to Eq. (7.12). The same result, $R = r$, therefore applies. In other words, the optimum load impedance $(R + jX)$ which causes maximum real power to be dissipated in it is given by

$$(R + jX) = (r - jx) \tag{7.15}$$

The load impedance is clearly the conjugate of the source impedance, and when Eq. (7.15) applies, a circuit is said to be *conjugate matched*. A moment's consideration shows that conjugate matching effectively resonates the source and load circuit, in that the voltage V and current I in Fig. 7.8 are in phase. Since the reactances cancel, the source and load resistors define the current, i.e., $I = \frac{V}{2r}$. Thus $P_{max} = |I|^2 r = \frac{|V|^2}{4r}$ as before

Example

Design a load circuit which will provide a conjugate match for the circuit shown in Fig. 7.9 at a frequency of 10^6 rad/s.

At $\omega = 10^6$ rad/s, the inductor has an impedance of $j \times 10^6 \times 10^{-3} = j10^3 \; \Omega$.

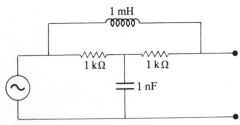

Fig. 7.9 Circuit example

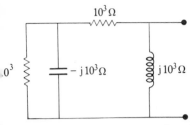

Fig. 7.10 Calculation of the source impedance for Fig. 7.9

while the capacitive impedance is $\dfrac{-j1}{(10^6 \times 10^{-9})} = -j10^3\ \Omega$. The Thévenin equivalent source impedance is therefore that of the circuit shown in Fig. 7.10. The capacitor and resistor have a combined impedance of $\dfrac{(-j10^3 \cdot 10^3)}{(10^3 - j10^3)} = (0.5 - j0.5)10^3\ \Omega$. With the 1 kΩ resistor in series, this increases to $(1.5 - j0.5)10^3\ \Omega$, and finally the shunt inductance gives a Thévenin source impedance of

$$\frac{j10^3 \times (1.5 - j0.5)10^3}{j10^3 + (1.5 - j0.5)10^3} = \frac{(0.5 + j1.5)10^3}{(1.5 + j0.5)} = (600 + j800)\Omega$$

For a conjugate match, a load impedance of $(600 - j800)\ \Omega$ is required. Since the reactive part is negative, the impedance may be realised as a series connection of a resistor of value 600 Ω, and a capacitor having reactance $-\dfrac{1}{\omega C} = -800\ \Omega$ at 10^6 rad/s. The capacitor value is therefore $C = \dfrac{1}{(10^6 \times 800)} = 1.25$ nF. Alternatively, we may work with the admittance of the required load. This will be $\dfrac{1}{(600 - j800)} = (6 + j8)10^{-4}$S. This admittance can be realised as the parallel combination of a conductance of 0.6 mS $(\equiv 1.67$ kΩ$)$ and a capacitive susceptance of $\omega C = 0.8$ mS. Thus $C = \dfrac{8 \times 10^{-4}}{10^6} = 0.8$ nF. The two alternative load circuits are shown in Fig. 7.11.

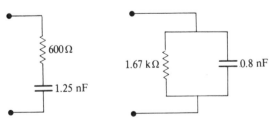

Fig. 7.11 Alternative load circuits for conjugate matching

In some circumstances, the resistive and reactive parts of a load impedance may not both be available as variables for calculating the power matched conditions, or the load circuit may be a specified configuration with some of the components fixed. In such cases, as in those considered in this section, maximum power transfer from source to load may be established by developing an expression for the real power in the load, and maximising it with respect to the available variables.

7.3   SUMMARY

The phase shifts between voltage and current which are introduced by reactive components in circuits excited with sinusoids have been shown in this chapter to lead to three types of power. The apparent power, obtained by taking the product of the magnitudes of the voltage and current supplied to a circuit is generally larger than either the real power dissipated in the circuit, or the reactive power, which is the maximum instantaneous power supplied to the reactive components in the circuit. The factor by which the real power is less than the apparent power is known as the power factor, and it has been shown that power factor correction can be accomplished by modifying a complex load impedance in order to bring the power factor closer to its ideal value of unity. A simple means of calculating a.c. power using the phasor representation of sinusoidal signals has been discussed, providing a useful extension to the tool of phasor analysis.

The problem of power transfer from source to load has also been treated, giving rise to the important concept of power matching and in particular conjugate matching for sources with complex source impedances.

Problems

1. When a 240 V (r.m.s.) 50 Hz mains supply is connected to a load impedance, a current of 3 A flows, lagging the voltage by 40°. Calculate (a) the apparent power, (b) the real power, (c) the reactive power, (d) the power factor and (e) the impedance of the load in rectangular form.
   (Answer: (a) 720 VA, (b) 551.6 W, (c) 462.8 VAr, (d) 0.766 lagging, (e) $(61.3 + j51.4)\,\Omega$).

2. A current $(5 - j6)$ mA flowing in an impedance develops a voltage $(4 + j2)$ V between its terminals. Calculate the apparent, real and reactive powers, together with the power factor.
   (Answer: 35 mVA, 8 mW, 34 mVAr, 0.229)

3. Find the value of capacitor which must be connected in parallel with the load described in question 1 above, such that the power factor is 0.95 lagging.
   (Answer: 15.5 μF)

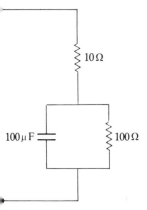

Fig. 7.12 Circuit example for problem 4

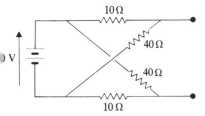

Fig. 7.13 Circuit example for problem 5

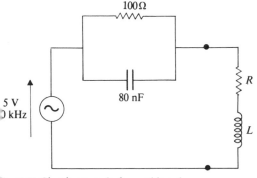

Fig. 7.14 Circuit example for problem 6

The circuit shown in Fig. 7.12 is to be connected to a 50 Hz supply. Calculate the power factor of the load, and the value of component which must be connected in parallel with the load to correct this to unity power factor.
(Answer: 0.3 leading; a 132.6 mH inductor)

Determine the value of load resistance which will extract the maximum power from the circuit of Fig. 7.13. What is the maximum power?
(Answer: 16 Ω, 1.56 W)

6. Find the values of the load components R and L in Fig. 7.14 such that the maximum real power is dissipated in the load, and determine that power. (Answer: R = 79.8 Ω, L = 638.6 μH, 62.5 mW)

7. Design a simple load circuit for the circuit in Fig. 7.15 to optimize the load power dissipation. The current source is operating at 50 Hz. (Answer: $R = 57.6\ \Omega$ in series with $C = 145\ \mu$F, or $R = 65.9\ \Omega$ in parallel with $C = 18.4\ \mu$F)

8. A nonideal current source has an internal impedance $(r + jx)\ \Omega$. A load impedance $(R + jX)\ \Omega$ is connected to the source, where $X = KR$. Find the expression for the value of R which would extract maximum real power from the source.

$$\left(\text{Answer: } R = \sqrt{\frac{r^2 + x^2}{1 - K^2}}\right)$$

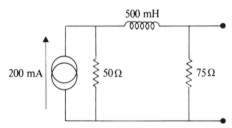

Fig. 7.15 Circuit example for problem 7

8

ANALYSIS WITH COMPLEX
WAVEFORMS

The circuit analysis techniques discussed in the preceding chapters of this book have dealt with those cases where the input has been a simple function of time. For example, when dealing with the transient response of circuits, the responses to step and ramp inputs were considered, while the phasor technique was developed for the special case of finding the steady state response under sinusoidal excitation.

When the inputs to circuits are represented by more complex functions of time, circuit analysis becomes less straightforward. Although there are many cases where the responses may still be found by solving the differential equations using the techniques which have been discussed, or by using more sophisticated mathematics tools such as the Laplace Transform, the calculations can nevertheless be tedious. In some cases, one must turn to the computer for help, using some numerical technique to compute the desired response. However, there is a special class of functions which represent signals which are often found in electronics. These are *periodic functions*, that is functions of time which regularly repeat themselves with some time interval, or *period*. Fig. 8.1 shows several typical periodic functions of time. All of these functions have a period of T time units. The interesting property of such periodic functions is that they can be shown to be composed of an infinite number of harmonically related sinusoids. The term *harmonic* here means that all the sinusoids have a frequency which is an integer multiple of the *fundamental* frequency, that is the frequency of repetition of the periodic signal. This property, which resulted from the work of the French mathematician Fourier is of great importance in many engineering subjects. In the context of circuit analysis, we shall see in this chapter that Fourier analysis helps to simplify the calculation of the response of circuits to periodic signals.

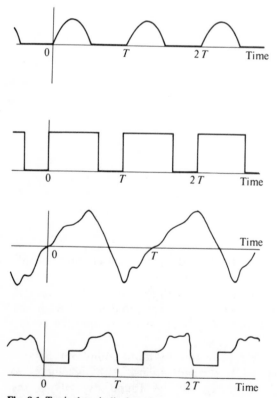

Fig. 8.1 Typical periodic functions

8.1   FOURIER ANALYSIS OF PERIODIC SIGNALS

If a time function $f(t)$ is periodic, then it satisfies the identity

$$f(t + T) = f(t), \quad -\infty \le t \le +\infty \qquad (8.1)$$

where T is the period. The bounds on the time t in Eq. (8.1) show that the function will be assumed to be periodic over an infinite time scale for the development which follows. This is why the waveforms in Fig. 8.1 are continued to the left of the zero time origin. If a signal expressed as a function of time satisfies Eq. (8.1), then Fourier showed that it could be expressed as a series

$$f(t) = a_0 + \sum_{k=1}^{\infty} a_k \cos(k\omega t) + \sum_{k=1}^{\infty} b_k \sin(k\omega t) \qquad (8.2)$$

In Eq. (8.2), ω represents the fundamental frequency of the periodic waveform in rad/s. It is the frequency of the sinusoid which has the same period as the periodic signal. Thus if the period T is measured in seconds, $\omega T = 2\pi$. A sinusoid having this frequency ω is often said to be the *fundamental* of the periodic waveform. As k takes on the value 2, 3, 4, etc., in Eq. (8.2), then the corresponding frequencies 2ω, 3ω, 4ω, etc., and often the associated sinusoids themselves, are referred to as the second-, third-, and fourth *harmonics* respectively.

The coefficients a_k and b_k are the amplitudes of the various sinusoids. Thus a_1 is the amplitude of the fundamental cosinewave $\cos(\omega t)$, b_3 is the amplitude of the third harmonic sinewave $\sin(3\omega t)$ and so forth. A constant term is also included in Eq. (8.2), and this is represented by the coefficient a_0. The significance of this term will presently become clear.

The Fourier analysis of a complex periodic waveform therefore requires the coefficients a_0, a_k and b_k to be found in Eq. (8.2). However, before we go on to discover how these may be found, it is important to consider the motivation for the use of Fourier analysis in the calculation of circuit response. This motivation may be explained with the help of Fig. 8.2. A periodic voltage $v_{in}(t)$ is shown as input to a circuit in Fig. 8.2(a). The response of the circuit will be taken to be the output voltage $v_o(t)$, although in what follows either input or output could be a current or a voltage without affecting the reasoning. Now if $v_{in}(t)$ is represented by a Fourier series as in Eq. (8.2), then it will consist of a constant term (corresponding to a d.c. voltage of magnitude a_0) added to a sum of sinusoidal voltages at the fundamental and an infinite number of harmonics frequencies. In other words, $v_{in}(t)$ can be represented by an infinite number of voltage sources connected in series, as shown in Fig. 8.2(b). The motivation for the exercise should become clear to the reader at this point, since the principle of superposition can now be invoked to find $v_o(t)$ by considering each of the input sources in turn. Since, according to Eq. (8.1), each of these

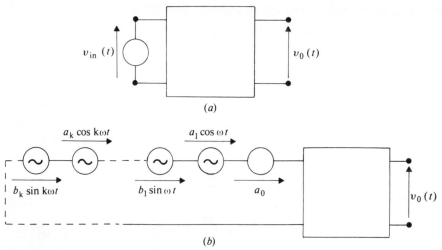

Fig. 8.2 Circuit with a periodic input signal

sources has been providing its output since the origin of time, $t = -\infty$, it is the sinusoidal steady state response which will be calculated for each source, using the phasor technique. In view of the infinity of sources at the input to the circuit, the reader may baulk at the apparent enormity of this task. In practice, however, each component of the output corresponding to a particular input source is often found to be of a standard form which rapidly becomes evident as the analysis proceeds. In addition, the amplitude of all but a few of the output components are often sufficiently small to be ignored.

We may now return to the problem of calculating the unknown coefficients a_o, a_k and b_k in the Fourier series of a function $f(t)$ as expressed by Eq. (8.2). To do this, appeal is made to the so-called *orthogonality* properties of sinusoids. First note that for all integer n,

$$\int_0^T \cos(n\omega t) \cdot dt = \int_0^T \sin(n\omega t) \cdot dt = 0 \qquad (8.3)$$

Now consider the following integral for integer n and m:

$$\int_0^T \cos(n\omega t) \cos(m\omega t) \cdot dt$$

$$= \int_0^T \frac{1}{2} \{\cos[(n+m)\omega t] + \cos[(n-m)\omega t]\} \, dt$$

$$= \frac{1}{2}\int_0^T \cos[(n+m)\omega t] \cdot dt + \frac{1}{2}\int_0^T \cos[(n-m)\omega t] \cdot dt \qquad (8.4)$$

By Eq. (8.3), the first integral in Eq. (8.4) will be zero. This will also be true for the second integral in Eq. (8.4), except for the case where $n = m$. In this case the second integral becomes

$$\frac{1}{2}\int_0^T 1 \cdot dt = \frac{T}{2}$$

In other words,

$$\int_0^T \cos{(n\omega t)} \cos{(m\omega t)} \cdot dt = \begin{cases} 0, & n \neq m \\ \dfrac{T}{2}, & n = m \end{cases} \tag{8.5}$$

There is a large class of mathematical functions which give a similar result to that stated for cosinusoids in Eq. (8.5). Such functions are said to be *orthogonal*. For the case in hand, the following results may also be simply derived:

$$\int_0^T \sin{(n\omega t)} \sin{(m\omega t)} \cdot dt = \begin{cases} 0, & n \neq m \\ \dfrac{T}{2}, & n = m \end{cases} \tag{8.6}$$

$$\int_0^T \cos{(n\omega t)} \sin{(m\omega t)}\, dt = 0, \text{ for all } n \text{ and } m \tag{8.7}$$

To find a_o in Eq. 8.2, the equation may be integrated with respect to time, to give

$$\int_0^T f(t)\, dt = \int_0^T a_o\, dt + \sum_{k=1}^\infty a_k \int_0^T \cos{(k\omega t)}\, dt + \sum_{k=1}^\infty b_k \int_0^T \sin{(k\omega t)}\, dt$$

Using Eq. (8.3) this becomes

$$\int_0^T f(t) \cdot dt = a_o T$$

i.e.,

$$a_o = \frac{1}{T}\int_0^T f(t) \cdot dt \tag{8.8}$$

We see that a_o is the mean value of the periodic function, evaluated over one period.

If now $f(t)$ is multiplied by $\cos{(n\omega t)}$ for some integer n, then Eq. (8.2) may be written as

$$f(t) \cos{(n\omega t)} = a_o \cos{(n\omega t)} + a_n \cos^2{(n\omega t)} + \sum_{\substack{k=1 \\ k \neq n}}^\infty a_k \cos{(k\omega t)} \cos{(n\omega t)}$$

$$+ \sum_{k=1}^\infty b_k \sin{(k\omega t)} \cos{(n\omega t)} \tag{8.9}$$

Integrating Eq. (8.9) over one period, and using Eq. (8.5) and Eq. (8.7), it will be seen that

$$\int_0^T f(t) \cos (n\omega t) \, dt = a_n \frac{T}{2}$$

i.e.,

$$a_n = \frac{2}{T} \int_0^T f(t) \cos (n\omega t) \cdot dt \tag{8.10}$$

Eq. (8.10) is a general result for the coefficient a_n. To find a general coefficient b_n, $f(t)$ may be multiplied by $\sin (n\omega t)$, and the integration repeated. The reader may care to confirm that in this case

$$b_n = \frac{2}{T} \int_0^T f(t) \sin (n\omega t) \cdot dt \tag{8.11}$$

To sum up, the Fourier coefficients may be found by evaluating the integrals in Eqs. (8.12).

$$\left. \begin{aligned} a_0 &= \frac{1}{T} \int_0^T f(t) \cdot dt \\[1em] a_n &= \frac{2}{T} \int_0^T f(t) \cos (n\omega t) \cdot dt \\[1em] b_n &= \frac{2}{T} \int_0^T f(t) \sin (n\omega t) \cdot dt \end{aligned} \right\} \tag{8.12}$$

As an example of the evaluation of these Fourier coefficients, consider the square wave $v(t)$ shown in Fig. 8.3. The amplitude of the waveform is E volts. Then using Eqs. (8.12),

$$a_0 = \int_0^T v(t) \cdot dt = \frac{1}{T} \int_0^{T/2} E \cdot dt = \frac{E}{2}$$

$$a_n = \frac{2}{T} \int_0^T v(t) \cos (n\omega t) \cdot dt = \frac{2E}{T} \int_0^{T/2} \cos (n\omega t) \cdot dt$$

$$= \frac{2E}{n\omega T} [\sin (n\omega t)]_0^{T/2}$$

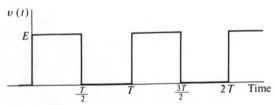

Fig. 8.3 Pulse waveform for Fourier analysis

Now $\omega T = 2\pi$, and so

$$a_n = \frac{E}{n\pi} [\sin(n\pi) - \sin(0)] = 0 \text{ for all } n$$

Next,

$$b_n = \frac{2}{T} \int_0^{T/2} v(t) \sin(n\omega t) \cdot dt = \frac{2E}{T} \int_0^{T/2} \sin(n\omega t) \cdot dt$$

$$= \frac{-2E}{n\omega T} [\cos n\omega t]_0^{T/2} = \frac{-E}{n\pi} [\cos(n\pi) - \cos(0)]$$

Thus

$$b_n = \begin{cases} \dfrac{2E}{n\pi} & \text{for } n \text{ odd} \\[2mm] 0 & \text{for } n \text{ even} \end{cases}$$

The Fourier series for the square wave is therefore

$$v(t) = \frac{E}{2} + \frac{2E}{\pi} \left(\sin \omega t + \frac{1}{3} \sin 3\omega t + \frac{1}{5} \sin 5\omega t + \cdots \right) \qquad (8.13)$$

The way in which the series expressed by Eq. (8.13) builds up into a full representation of the square wave is shown in Fig. 8.4. Here the waveforms corresponding to the summation of just a few terms in the series are shown, starting with one term $\left(\dfrac{E}{2} \right)$, then adding $\dfrac{(2E \sin \omega t)}{\pi}$, and so on up to the fifth harmonic. It is seen that the general shape of the final waveform becomes rapidly apparent.

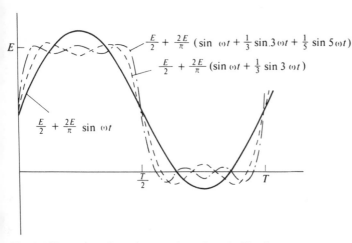

Fig. 8.4 Formation of a pulse waveform from its Fourier components

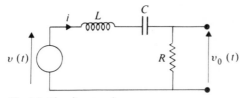

Fig. 8.5 Circuit example

Having obtained the Fourier Series of a waveform, it may be used as required for circuit analysis. For example, Fig. 8.5 shows a simple tuned circuit driven from a voltage source whose waveform is that of Fig. 8.3, and can therefore be expressed by Eq. (8.13). The problem is to find the output voltage $v_o(t)$. Now for a sinusoidal input, the output phasor $V_o(j\Omega)$ is related to the input $V_{in}(j\Omega)$ at a frequency Ω rad/s according to

$$V_o = V_{in}\frac{R}{R + j\left(\Omega L - \dfrac{1}{\Omega C}\right)} \tag{8.14}$$

Using $\omega_o = \dfrac{1}{\sqrt{LC}}$, and $Q = \dfrac{\omega_o L}{R}$, Eq. (8.14) may be written in the general form

$$V_o = V_{in} \cdot \frac{1}{1 + jQ\left(\dfrac{\Omega}{\omega_o} - \dfrac{\omega_o}{\Omega}\right)} \tag{8.15}$$

where ω_o is the resonant frequency of the circuit.

For the purposes of the example we shall take the resonant frequency of the tuned circuit to be five times the fundamental frequency of the applied squarewave, i.e., $\omega_o = 5\omega$, and assume $Q = 100$. Each sinusoidal component of the input waveform may now be considered in turn, from Eq. (8.13), and Eq. (8.15) may be used to compute the output. For the d.c. component ($\Omega = 0$), then clearly $V_o = 0$. However, for $\Omega = \omega$, the fundamental frequency, Eq. (8.15) becomes

$$V_o = \frac{2E}{\pi} \cdot \frac{1}{1 + j100\left(\dfrac{\omega}{5\omega} - \dfrac{5\omega}{\omega}\right)} = 1.33 \times 10^{-3}E\,\underline{/89.9°}$$

Repeating this calculation for $\Omega = 3\omega$, 5ω, etc., leads to the results shown in Table 8.1. It will be seen that the magnitude of the output phasor corresponding to each input component is small compared with the magnitude at $\Omega = 5\omega$. This of course is the resonant frequency of the tuned circuit. As Ω increases above 9ω, these magnitudes become even smaller. For all practical purposes, therefore, the output of the tuned circuit will be $v_o(t) = 0.127 \sin 5\omega t$.

Table 8.1

Ω	$\dfrac{V_o}{E}$
ω	$1.33 \times 10^{-3} \underline{/89.9°}$
3ω	$1.99 \times 10^{-3} \underline{/89.5°}$
5ω	$0.127 \underline{/0°}$
7ω	$1.33 \times 10^{-3} \underline{/-89.2°}$
9ω	$5.68 \times 10^{-4} \underline{/-89.5°}$

In effect the high Q of the tuned circuit, and hence its high selectivity, has led to the circuit picking out just the sinusoidal component of the square wave which is at its resonant frequency. If this frequency were changed, perhaps by varying C, then other harmonics, or even the fundamental could be selected. Provided the circuit Q was kept high, little distortion of the output waveform would result from the response of the circuit to other input components. Waveforms such as the squarewave which are rich in harmonics are frequently used as a source of harmonically related sinusoids in multiband radio transmitters.

Example

Find the Fourier series for the voltage waveform shown in Fig. 8.6(a), and determine the output of the circuit shown in Fig. 8.6(b) when this signal is applied as its input.

It will be seen that the waveform consists of a series of halfsinewaves such as are obtained from the full wave rectification of a sinewave of period $2T$. The waveform is therefore the repetition of the positive half cycles of the signal $E \sin \dfrac{\omega t}{2}$, where $\omega T = 2\pi$ as usual. Using Eq. (8.12),

$$a_o = \frac{1}{T} \int_0^T E \sin \frac{\omega t}{2} \cdot dt = \frac{E}{T} \left[-\frac{2}{\omega} \cos \frac{\omega t}{2} \right]_0^T = \frac{2E}{\pi}$$

while

$$a_n = \frac{2E}{T} \int_0^T \sin \frac{\omega t}{2} \cos n\omega t \cdot dt$$

$$= \frac{E}{T} \int_0^T \left\{ \sin \left[\left(n + \frac{1}{2} \right) \omega t \right] - \sin \left[\left(n - \frac{1}{2} \right) \omega t \right] \right\} \cdot dt$$

Straightforward evaluation of the above integral reveals

$$a_n = \frac{4}{\pi(1 - 4n^2)}$$

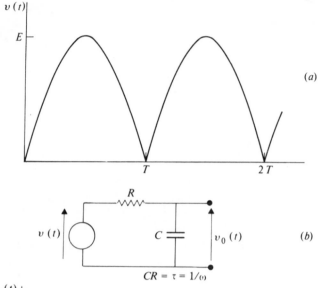

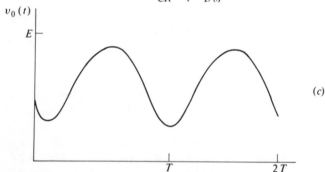

Fig. 8.6 (*a*) Full wave rectified sinusoid, (*b*) circuit example, (*c*) output waveform when signal (*a*) is applied to the circuit

Similarly

$$b_n = \frac{2E}{T} \int_0^T \sin \frac{\omega t}{2} \sin n\omega t \cdot dt$$

$$= \frac{E}{T} \int_0^T \left\{ \cos \left[\left(n - \frac{1}{2} \right) \omega t \right] - \cos \left[\left(n + \frac{1}{2} \right) \omega t \right] \right\} \cdot dt$$

Further manipulation gives $b_n = 0$. The Fourier series for the waveform is therefore

$$v(t) = \frac{2E}{\pi} + \sum_{k=1}^{\infty} \frac{4E}{\pi(1 - 4k^2)} \cos k\omega t \tag{8.16}$$

$$= \frac{2E}{\pi} - \frac{4E}{\pi} \left[\frac{1}{3} \cos \omega t + \frac{1}{15} \cos 2\omega t + \frac{1}{35} \cos 3\omega t + \cdots \right] \tag{8.17}$$

To find the response of the circuit of Fig. 8.6(b), first note that its output voltage at a frequency Ω is given by

$$V_o = V_{in} \cdot \frac{1}{1 + j\Omega CR} = V_{in} \cdot \frac{1}{1 + j\Omega\tau} \qquad (8.18)$$

In the steady state the d.c. component $\left(\frac{2}{\pi} E = 0.64E\right)$ in Eq. (8.16) will be transmitted from input to output without being affected, while for the general term in this equation at frequency $k\omega$, Eq. (8.18) gives

$$V_o = \frac{4E}{\pi(1 - 4k^2)} \cdot \frac{1}{1 + jk\omega\tau} = \frac{4E}{\pi(4k^2 - 1)(1 + k^2)^{1/2}} \underline{/180° - \tan^{-1} k}$$

Values of V_o for various k are given in Table 8.2. In this case the fundamental has a magnitude about eight times that of the second harmonic, and more than twenty times that of the third harmonic. Further harmonics are even smaller. To a first approximation therefore, the output voltage is given by

$$V(t) = E[0.64 + 0.3 \cos(\omega t + 2.36) + 3.8 \times 10^{-2} \cos(2\omega t + 2.04)] \qquad (8.19)$$

Note that the arguments of the fundamental and second harmonic outputs in Table 8.2 have been converted to radians in Eq. (8.19). Eq. (8.19) is plotted in Fig. 8.6(c).

It will have been noted that no cosine terms were present in the Fourier series for the squarewave, while no sine terms appeared in the series for the rectified sinewave in the example above. The rectified sinewave shown in Fig. 8.6 is an example of an *even function*. An even function f(t) has the property f(t) = f($-t$), and so if f(t) is represented by a Fourier series

$$f(t) = a_o + \sum_{k=1}^{\infty} a_k \cos(k\omega t) + \sum_{k=1}^{\infty} b_k \sin(k\omega t) \qquad (8.20)$$

Table 8.2

k	$\dfrac{V_o}{E}$
1	$0.30 \underline{/135.0°}$
2	$3.80 \times 10^{-2} \underline{/116.6°}$
3	$1.15 \times 10^{-2} \underline{/108.4°}$
4	$4.90 \times 10^{-3} \underline{/104.0°}$
5	$2.52 \times 10^{-3} \underline{/101.3°}$

then

$$f(-t) = a_o + \sum_{k=1}^{\infty} a_k \cos(-k\omega t) + \sum_{k=1}^{\infty} b_k \sin(-k\omega t)$$

$$= a_o + \sum_{k=1}^{\infty} a_k \cos k\omega t - \sum_{k=1}^{\infty} b_k \sin(k\omega t) \qquad (8.21)$$

Equating Eq. (8.20) and Eq. (8.21), gives

$$2 \sum_{1}^{\infty} b_k \sin(k\omega t) = 0, \quad \text{i.e., } b_k = 0, \ k = 1, 2 \ldots \infty$$

The Fourier series for an even function will therefore never contain any sine terms.

A function which has the property $f(t) = -f(-t)$ is known as an *odd function*. By a similar argument to that above, it can simply be shown that the Fourier series of an odd function will contain only sine terms—there are no cosine terms and no d.c. component in such a series. Thus the square wave shown in Fig. 8.3 is not an odd function, since clearly $v(-t) \neq -v(t)$, and this is borne out by Eq. (8.13), which contains the d.c. component $\frac{E}{2}$. However, if this d.c. component is removed, then the waveform of Fig. 8.7 results, which clearly has the required odd property.

From the computational point of view, it is useful if a waveform can be recognised as being that of an even or odd function, or if adjustment of the d.c. level of a waveform can be seen to render it an odd function, since only the cosine or the sine coefficients then need to be calculated. In many cases of course, a waveform will correspond to neither an odd nor an even function. Fig. 8.8 for example shows a periodic waveform which fits this category, and which represents the repetition of the curve $e^{-t/T}$ every period T. The reader may care to confirm that this waveform has the Fourier series

$$f(t) = (1 - e^{-1}) \left[1 + \sum_{k=1}^{\infty} \frac{2}{1 + 4\pi^2 k^2} \cos(k\omega t) + \sum_{k=1}^{\infty} \frac{4\pi k}{1 + 4\pi^2 k^2} \sin(k\omega t) \right]$$

$$(8.22)$$

When a Fourier series contains both cosine and sine terms, as in Eq.

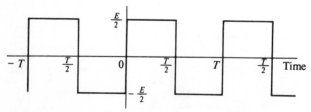

Fig. 8.7 Pulse waveform without a d.c. component

Fig. 8.8 Periodic waveform which corresponds to a function which is neither odd nor even

(8.22), some simplification can be obtained by combining the terms corresponding to the same frequency. For example, the general kth harmonic term in Eq. (8.2) is $a_k \cos(k\omega t) + b_k \sin(k\omega t)$. This may be written as

$$(a_k^2 + b_k^2)^{1/2} \left[\frac{a_k}{(a_k^2 + b_k^2)^{1/2}} \cos(k\omega t) + \frac{b_k}{(a_k^2 + b_k^2)^{1/2}} \sin(k\omega t) \right]$$

$$= (a_k^2 + b_k^2)^{1/2} \sin(k\omega t + \theta_k), \text{ where } \theta_k = \tan^{-1}\left(\frac{a_k}{b_k}\right) \qquad (8.23)$$

Eq. (8.2) may then be written as

$$f(t) = a_o + \sum_{k=1}^{\infty} (a_k^2 + b_k^2)^{1/2} \sin(k\omega t + \theta_k) \qquad (8.24)$$

In the general case, Eq. (8.24) may be used in preference to Eq. (8.2) when calculating the output of a circuit due to some signal input. The quantity $(a_k^2 + b_k^2)^{1/2}$ represents the magnitude of the kth harmonic. Frequently these magnitudes are plotted against frequency to show the *spectrum* of a signal. The spectrum is a frequency domain representation of the signal which is equivalent to the time domain waveforms. Strictly, of course, the phase spectrum should accompany the magnitude spectrum to give a complete frequency domain description of a signal. As examples, Fig. 8.9 shows the magnitude spectra of the square wave, rectified sinewave and the exponential waveform discussed above. These spectra are known as *discrete*, or *line* spectra, for obvious reasons. As the period T of a waveform is made larger, and hence the spacing $\omega = \frac{1}{T}$ of the spectral lines becomes smaller, the spectrum loses its discrete appearance, until with infinite period, the spectrum becomes truly continuous. Thus, with more advanced treatment, even waveforms with infinite period (that is those which are strictly not periodic in finite time) can be represented in the frequency domain, although the mathematics (which uses the *Fourier transform*) is beyond the scope of this book.

The important point to note is that a periodic signal may be characterised in either the time domain (as a waveform or a function of time) or in the frequency domain (as a spectrum). The characterizations are entirely equivalent, and will therefore predict the same steady state response when

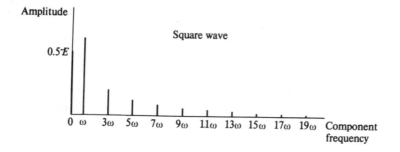

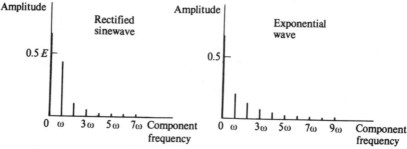

Fig. 8.9 Magnitude spectra of various waveforms

used for circuit analysis. For example, the square wave applied to the tuned circuit shown in Fig. 8.5 was shown to give a response at the fifth harmonic of the fundamental frequency which because of the high Q was almost a pure sinusoid. This result was achieved in the frequency domain. An alternative approach to the problem of calculating the response to the input waveform lies in the time domain. The time domain relationship between output and input voltage in the tuned circuit is given by

$$v(t) = L\frac{di}{dt} + \frac{1}{C}\int_0^t i\,dt + iR$$

Differentiating, and using $v_o = iR$,

$$\frac{L}{R}\frac{d^2v_o}{dt^2} + \frac{dv_o}{dt} + \frac{v_o}{CR} = \frac{dv}{dt}$$

Noting $\omega_o^2 = \dfrac{1}{LC}$, $Q = \dfrac{\omega_o L}{R}$, this equation may be written as

$$\frac{d^2v_o}{dt^2} + \frac{\omega_o}{Q}\frac{dv_o}{dt} + \omega_o^2 v_o = \frac{\omega_o}{Q}\frac{dv}{dt} \tag{8.25}$$

Now the square wave shown in Fig. 8.3 may be represented in the time domain by the superposition of a series of positive and negative step

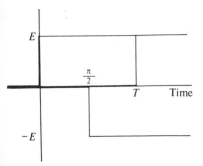

Fig. 8.10 Superposition of step functions to give a square waveform

functions with amplitude E volts as shown in Fig. 8.10. This point was discussed in Chapter 2. The solution of Eq. (8.25) to each of these steps may be found, and the solutions superimposed to give the final result. Using the methods of Chapter 2, and noting that $Q = 100$ and $\omega_0 = 5\omega$, the solution of Eq. (8.25) to a step of amplitude E volts at time $t = 0$ s is found to be

$$v_o(t) = \frac{E}{Q} e^{-(5\omega/2Q)t} \sin\left[5\omega\left(1 - \frac{1}{4Q^2}\right)^{1/2} t\right] \approx \frac{E}{Q} e^{-(5\omega/2Q)t} \sin(5\omega t).$$

After a time $\frac{T}{2}$, the response to the negative going step, namely

$-\dfrac{E}{Q} e^{-(5\omega/2Q)(t - T/2)} \sin\left[5\omega\left(t - \dfrac{T}{2}\right)\right] = \dfrac{E}{Q} e^{-(5\omega/2Q)(t - T/2)} \sin(5\omega t)$ must be added,

and so on, after each half period. If an attempt is made to sum the series which results, and if $t \to \infty$ (remember we are seeking the steady state response), then a rather complex algebraic development shows that the steady state response is $v_o(t) = 0.127 \sin 5\omega t$. This of course is precisely the result previously obtained in the frequency domain. The proof of this is not important here, and has been omitted for the sake of brevity. However it is important to appreciate the two approaches afforded by the characterization of signals in the frequency domain and the time domain, and the fact that often (as in the above case), the frequency domain provides the simpler approach.

8.2 SUMMARY

By considering their Fourier Series, we have seen that periodic signals may be expressed as an infinite sum of harmonically related sinusoids, together with a d.c. term. If such a periodic signal is applied as the input to a circuit, then each of the sinusoidal components may be considered in turn, and the circuit output to that component computed. For the purposes of Fourier analysis the signal is considered to have existed since the origin of time, $t = -\infty$, and so phasor analysis is appropriate to give the steady state sinusoidal response, since the transient response may be assumed to have decayed to zero after such a time. The principle of superposition may then be invoked to give the response to the periodic input as the sum of the individual responses found in their way.

Fourier analysis is clearly a useful tool which extends the range of circuit analysis problems which may be simply solved by the engineer. In addition, however, it clearly demonstrates the relationship between the time domain and the frequency domain as alternative means of describing signals; in the time domain a signal may be characterised by a function of time, or by its graphed waveform, whilst in the frequency domain it is equivalently characterized by the magnitudes and phases of its Fourier components. In essence, this is all that there is to the concepts of time and frequency domain. However, despite the apparent simplicity, the concepts hold a position of great importance in more advanced studies in electronic engineering.

Problems

1. Find the Fourier series for the rectangular pulse train shown in Fig. 8.11.
$$\left(\text{Answer: } f(t) = \frac{W}{T} + \sum_{n=1}^{\infty} \frac{1}{n\pi} \sin\left(\frac{2\pi nW}{T}\right) \cos(n\omega t) \right.$$
$$\left. + \sum_{n=1}^{\infty} \frac{1}{n\pi} \left[1 - \cos\left(\frac{2\pi nW}{T}\right) \right] \sin(n\omega t) \right)$$

2. One cycle of a repetitive waveform is shown in Fig. 8.12. Calculate the amplitude of the third harmonic of this waveform. (Answer: 0.168)

3. The waveform shown in Fig. 8.13 is obtained by switching off a sinusoidal signal after a time $t = \alpha$ seconds in each cycle. Find the coefficients of the fundamental components of the Fourier series for this waveform.
$$\left(\text{Answer: } b_1 = \frac{\alpha V}{T} - \frac{V}{4\pi} \sin\left(\frac{4\pi\alpha}{T}\right), \ a_1 = \frac{V}{4\pi}\left[1 - \cos\left(\frac{4\pi\alpha}{T}\right) \right] \right)$$

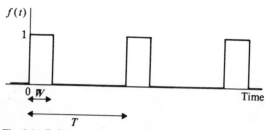

Fig. 8.11 Pulse waveform (problem 1)

4. A voltage $v_{in}(t)$ having waveform shown in Fig. 8.14(a) is applied to the circuit shown in Fig. 8.14(b). Find the Fourier coefficients for the steady state output voltage $v_o(t)$.

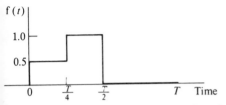

$$\left(\text{Answer: } v_o = \sum_{\substack{n=1 \\ n \text{ odd}}}^{\infty} \frac{4}{n\pi(1+0.39n^2)^{1/2}} \sin(2\pi n \times 10^3 t + \phi), \ \phi = \tan^{-1}(0.63n) \text{ rad} \right)$$

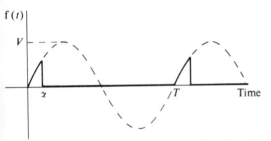

Fig. 8.12 One cycle of a repetitive waveform (problem 2)

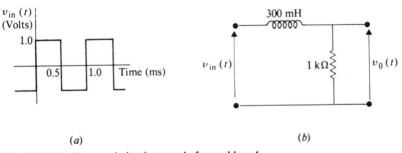

Fig. 8.13 Waveform derived from a sinusoidal signal (problem 3)

$v_{in}(t)$
(Volts)

1.0

0.5   1.0   Time (ms)

$v_{in}(t)$ 300 mH   1 kΩ $v_0(t)$

(a)   (b)

Fig. 8.14 Waveform and circuit example for problem 4

INDEX

Printed in Great Britain by Spottiswoode Ballantyne Ltd., Colchester and London